PRAEGER LIBRARY OF U.S. GOVERNMENT DEPARTMENTS
AND AGENCIES

The National Aeronautics and Space Administration

PRAEGER LIBRARY OF U.S. GOVERNMENT DEPARTMENTS
AND AGENCIES

Consulting Editors

ERNEST S. GRIFFITH

Former University Professor and Dean Emeritus, School of International Service, American University; former Director, Legislative Reference Service, Library of Congress; and author of *The American System of Government* and *The Modern Government in Action*

HUGH LANGDON ELSBREE

Former Chairman, Department of Political Science, Dartmouth College; former Managing Editor, *American Political Science Review;* former Director, Legislative Reference Service, Library of Congress

THE U.S. GOVERNMENT today is a maze of departments and agencies engaged in a world-wide range of programs and activities. Some departments are as old as the government itself; others are newly created or have been expanded or redirected by recent legislation. The books in this series describe the origin, development, function, methods, and structure of specific departments or agencies and explain how far their activities extend and how they relate to other branches of the government and to the public. All are written by authors with firsthand knowledge of their subjects.

The *Praeger Library of U.S. Government Departments and Agencies* is the only comprehensive, detailed source of such information. More than seventy titles are planned for the series; a list of those already published appears at the back of this volume.—THE EDITORS

The National Aeronautics and Space Administration

Richard Hirsch and
Joseph John Trento

PRAEGER PUBLISHERS
New York • Washington • London

629.454
H 669

PRAEGER PUBLISHERS
111 Fourth Avenue, New York, N.Y. 10003, U.S.A.
5, Cromwell Place, London SW7 2JL, England

Published in the United States of America in 1973
by Praeger Publishers, Inc.

© 1973 by Praeger Publishers, Inc.

Library of Congress Cataloging in Publication Data
Hirsch, Richard, 1912–71
The National Aeronautics and Space Administration.

(Praeger library of U. S. Government departments and agencies, no. 35)
Bibliography: p. 234
1. United States. National Aeronautics and Space Administration. I.
Trento, Joseph, 1947– joint author. II. Title.
TL789.8.U5H55   353.008'242   73-2920

This book is No. 35 in the series
Praeger Library of U.S. Government Departments and Agencies

Printed in the United States of America

Preface

This book is about the future and about exploration, the most stunningly exacting exploration man has ever undertaken. It is also about NASA, the federal agency that has been assigned the task of freeing man from the bonds of this planet and putting him in space—there, as President Kennedy put it, "to set sail on this new sea."

The late Richard Hirsch was aerospace assistant to the National Aeronautics and Space Council before his retirement. Although he died before reaching the halfway point in his manuscript, he must be given credit for many of the pages that follow. We never met, but his notes and files have been of great assistance in helping me complete his sections of the book as I think he might have done. I have never worked for NASA, but I have had numerous opportunities, as a journalist, to observe the operations of the agency at first hand. Since Mr. Hirsch's death in early 1971, hundreds of changes have taken place in NASA, and his chapters have been revised to reflect those changes.

In the process of writing this book, I have covered Apollo launches at Cape Kennedy in Florida, visited other NASA facilities, and interviewed hundreds of NASA officials, critics, and supporters. Throughout all the research and interviewing, I found that two early impressions of mine were well founded: that NASA had been brought into American life by Senator Lyndon Baines Johnson and that the agency had been given the momentum it needed to survive by President John F. Kennedy. NASA employees are convinced that without the efforts of these two men, the agency would have withered on the vine or been less than it is today. Although politics is not a major topic of discussion at NASA, the names of both men were mentioned in nearly every interview I conducted.

NASA is the easiest of federal agencies to inform oneself about. Its failures cannot be buried in a file to be discovered by some later government audit. If NASA fails to complete a major task, the American public is almost instantly made aware of it.

I have been asked by many persons, both inside and outside NASA, if I considered NASA glamorous. Some readers may consider "glamorous" demeaning, too lightweight a term to apply to an organization so firmly grounded in science and technology. Nevertheless, NASA *is* glamorous. It is also exciting. Its true significance, however, is based on something that goes far beyond glamour and excitement, and that is one of the things that Mr. Hirsch and I have attempted to demonstrate in this book. Undoubtedly it will be read for the facts and information it contains, but it was written in the hope that the reader will obtain a glimpse, beyond these pages, of what a remarkable adventure NASA has been—and must continue to be—for all of mankind.

Many people have assisted me in preparing this story of NASA. I want to thank three in particular, whose assistance far exceeded that required by normal courtesy—Louise Dick, Porter Brown, and Charles Mathews, all of NASA. I also want to thank Fred Howard at Praeger Publishers, who gave patient advice to me through the long process of completing the manuscript. Finally, I want to express my thanks to my wife, Judith, who shared the excitement of "the Cape" with me, as well as the routine of sifting through thousands of pages of documents concerning the agency.

La Jolla, California   JOSEPH JOHN TRENTO
February, 1973

Contents

A section of photographs follows page 86.
A NASA organization chart appears on page 47.

The National Aeronautics
and Space Administration

I

Before NASA

There were no TV cameras in evidence, and no ceremonial pens were handed out when President Woodrow Wilson signed the Naval Appropriations Act on March 3, 1915, with its rider establishing an Advisory Committee for Aeronautics. Although the Wright brothers had flown their Kitty Hawk craft in 1903, and the U.S. Army had purchased its first military airplane, a Wright Flyer, in 1909, the United States was the only major nation in the Western world without a governmental laboratory devoted to the science of flight.

The concept and even the name of the Advisory Committee were patterned after the British Advisory Committee for Aeronautics, which had been started in 1910. President Wilson appointed unsalaried members to the so-called Main Committee. They represented the military and naval air services, the Weather Bureau, the Smithsonian Institution, and the scientific community.

At its first meeting the Main Committee changed the name of the new organization to the National Advisory Committee for Aeronautics, and shortly afterward "NACA" began to make a survey of the state of aeronautical research and facilities in this country. Since Congress had appropriated the sum of $5,000 a year, or "so much thereof as may be necessary, for five years," there was barely enough money to hire the committee's clerk, John F. Victory, or to hold an occasional meeting.

FROM WORLD WAR I TO SUPERSONIC FLIGHT

The fact that no aircraft of U.S. design reached combat status during World War I illustrates the backwardness of U.S. aviation at the time NACA was created. Although NACA did serve as a focal point for defining policy problems and assigning research priorities, and made recommendations on cross-licensing of patents, on airmail service, and on aircraft production, it was not until after the war that it began its own historic wind tunnel and research efforts.

These endeavors were begun at Langley Field, Virginia, in 1920, and for the next two decades the Langley installation was NACA's sole laboratory. The work done there was outstanding. Basic aircraft design was revolutionized time and again by NACA's technical reports in the 1920's and the 1930's. NACA researchers were responsible for such innovations as the cantilevered aircraft wing, the all-metal airframe, the smooth cowling for radial engines, wing-mounted engine nacelles, and retractable landing gear.

During much of this same period, while NACA was perfecting its skills in aeronautics, an individual who shunned the institutional approach was laying the basis for the giant leap from aeronautics to astronautics. He was Robert H. Goddard, a professor of physics at Clark University in Worcester, Massachusetts, who took out his first patent on a multistage rocket in 1914. In 1916, he suggested that the moon could be hit by a rocket that would carry a flash bomb in its nose, so that the impact would be visible from earth. In 1918, he had demonstrated to the War Department how a tank could be put out of action by a rocket fired from a recoilless barrel carried by one man. Not until World War II was well under way did the U.S. begin to develop such a weapon—the bazooka. This revolutionary work went largely unnoticed, and Goddard spent the next twenty years quietly putting his theories into practice, perfecting no fewer than 214 patents, which covered the basic design of the airframes, fuel pumps, valves, and guidance devices necessary for flight.

Meanwhile young aeronautical and mechanical engineers just leaving college were drawn to NACA by the opportunity to do challenging research and to see their names on technical papers, and by the superior equipment at Langley Field. NACA itself was still small and inconspicuous—as late as the outbreak of World War II in the summer of 1939, its complement of staff was 532 people, of whom 278 were engaged in research, and its budget for that fiscal year was $4.6 million. This was in keeping with the prevailing mood of the country, which was concentrated on the domestic ills caused by the Great Depression. There was little interest in defense appropriations.

As the shadow of war moved closer to Europe, however, there were stirrings of interest in an expanded military establishment, including military aviation. As a result, NACA eventually secured funds to increase its effort, not only in aerodynamics but in propulsion and materials research. A new aeronautical laboratory, the Ames Research Center, named after physicist Joseph S. Ames of Johns Hopkins University, a former chairman of the Main Committee, was begun in 1940, on land adjacent to the Navy installation at Moffett Field, forty miles south of San Francisco. The next year, on a site next to the municipal airport at Cleveland, NACA broke ground for still another laboratory, to be devoted to engine research in later years. Called the Lewis Research Center, it was named after George W. Lewis, for twenty-eight years NACA's director of research.

Nine months before Pearl Harbor, NACA Chairman

Vannevar Bush appointed a Special Committee on Jet Propulsion, headed by former Main Committeeman William F. Durand of Stanford University, and including such leaders in aeronautical science as Theodor von Karman of the California Institute of Technology and Hugh L. Dryden of the National Bureau of Standards. Until then NACA, the military services, and the aircraft industry had given little attention to jet propulsion. There had been little active disagreement with the conclusion reached in 1923 by the Bureau of Standards: "Propulsion by the reaction of a simple jet cannot compete, in any respect, with air screw propulsion at such flying speeds as are now in prospect." By 1941, however, Germany had flown turbojets, and her researchers were working intensively on the development of an operational jet-propelled interceptor. In Britain, the propulsion scientist Frank Whittle had designed and built a gas-turbine engine and had flown a turbojet-powered aircraft.

Faced with the prospect of European-developed aircraft that could reach speeds in excess of 400 miles per hour and operational altitudes of about 40,000 feet, NACA gradually authorized more and more research on jet power plants for the Army Air Force and the Navy. Most of the NACA research effort during the war, however, went to "quick fixes," improving or "cleaning up" military aircraft already produced by aircraft companies, rather than to the more fundamental problems of aircraft design, construction, and propulsion. So, understandably and predictably, during World War II, Germany was first to put into operation military aircraft driven by jet power plants, as well as rocket-powered interceptors that could fly at 590 miles per hour and climb to 40,000 feet in two and one-half minutes. The German jets and rocket planes came into the war too late to have any effect on its outcome, but the new aircraft caused consternation among American aeronautical scientists and military planners.

As a result, NACA's wartime achievements were in conventional aircraft. Perhaps its major wartime contribution was its design (completed within ninety days, to British specifications) of the P-51 Mustang fighter plane, which has been called the best single-engine aircraft of the war. Its superior maneuverability and speed were based in large measure on NACA's laminar-flow wing design, itself the outcome of thousands of hours of wind tunnel research. It has been said that the Germans were never able to discover in their own wind tunnels why the P-51 was so fast and maneuverable.

With the recognition that propeller-driven aircraft had reached their performance limit, the military services and NACA began, in 1944, a cooperative airplane for research into transsonic and supersonic flight—the X-1, which was powered by a 6,000-pound thrust rocket burning liquid oxygen and a mixture of alcohol and distilled water. A Pilotless Aircraft Research Station was established at Wallops Island, Virginia, and in 1947, a High-Speed Flight Station was opened at Edwards Air Force Base in southern California. During that same year the X-1 made the first flight faster than the speed of sound.

NACA's focus remained on aeronautics, however, and it was largely as an extension of flight testing that it became involved in space. The NACA position toward rocketry was expressed by Jerome C. Hunsaker, a member of the Main Committee and for a while its chairman. "You can have the Buck Rogers jobs," he told a member of the California Institute of Technology when he was told that the Army Air Corps had contracted with the famed Theodor von Karman for rocket research. NACA's attitude toward astronautics was, in the words of the official history, "skeptical, conservative and reticent." The Pilotless Aircraft Research Station at Wallops Island was regarded essentially as a tool for aerodynamics research rather than a springboard into the space age. Its goal was to further supersonic flight within the atmosphere. Thus NACA's annual report for 1948 mentioned data on the heating of the nose cones of the V-8 rockets fired at White Sands Proving Ground in New Mexico in the context of aircraft structural problems.

However, at the request of the military services, all three of NACA's field research centers (Langley, Lewis, and Ames) were studying the theoretical performance of missiles, the operations of rocket engines, the composition of rocket fuels, and automatic control arrangements for supersonic guided missiles and aircraft, all of which had growth potential for space-related applications.

During this time, however, NACA began to slide downhill in terms of budget support. Small cuts, begun in 1949, peaked in 1954 when the agency received only half of its request. This trend intensified the conservatism of NACA's leaders, especially when during the Korean War the highest priority was placed on quick fixes to operating problems in military aircraft. There was such a declining support for anything remotely connected to space flight research that in 1953 Hugh Dryden wrote, "I am reasonably sure that travel to the moon will not occur in my lifetime."

Despite cold war pressures, which demanded quick fixes to operating military aircraft, NACA tried to direct its attention to fundamental aeronautical research. Here it soon became apparent that the outstanding bar to progress was the so-called sonic barrier near the speed of sound where an aircraft encounters compressibility phenomena in fluid mechanics, actually the piling up of air molecules. Wind tunnels were also affected by this barrier, and attempts to simulate flight conditions in the transsonic range, 600–800 miles per hour, resulted in a choking effect. As a consequence, NACA's primary research tool, the wind tunnel, had to be redesigned. Not until 1951 was a slotted-throat tunnel able to overcome this effect, and not until the mid-1950's did the supersonic tunnels of both NACA and the Air Force come into being. In the interim, NACA was forced to turn to other measures to get into transsonic research. One of these was the firing of small solid-propellant rockets to gather data on various aerodynamic shapes at speeds greater than Mach 1, the speed of sound. These rocket firings were carried out at the Wallops Island station for a research team led by Robert R. Gilruth, who later was to become head of the Manned Spacecraft center.

Toward Outer Space

Despite NACA's concentration on flight within the atmosphere, the tug toward space flight was a powerful one that could not be stilled. Starting in 1952, the congressional Committee on Aerodynamics proposed that NACA "devote a modest effort to problems associated with unmanned and manned flight at altitudes from fifty miles to infinity and at speeds from Mach 10 to the velocity of escape from the earth's gravity." Before long a team of three Langley Research Center engineers was asked to suggest a suitable manned vehicle for research into upper atmosphere and space flight problems. There was some objection from the director of the Ames Research Center, who felt that "a study group of any size is not warranted—there are many more pressing and realistic problems to be met and solved in the next ten years." Nevertheless the work at Langley did go on, and in July, 1954, a proposal was made to the Air Force and the Navy to join in a tripartite program for the manned exploration of the upper atmosphere, based on what came to be known as the X-15 project.

Even though the Ames director was skeptical of space investments, some of the most space-flight-oriented engineers working for NACA in the early 1950's were at the Ames Center. These were led by Harry Julian Allen, chief of the High-Speed Research Division, who was firing a gun-launched model upstream through a supersonic wind tunnel to study aerodynamic behavior at high Mach numbers. This facility constructed at an original cost of only $20,000 proved to be one of NACA's most valuable tools for hypersonic research at Mach 15, as it strove to solve problems of re-entry heating. It was Allen, working with his high-speed chamber, who first showed that the blunt body, not the streamlined shape, was the most efficient configuration for dissipating heat into the atmosphere. Although this conclusion seemed to contradict all of the years of research that had led to streamlined aircraft design, Allen published his findings in 1953 and received the NACA Distinguished Service Medal in 1957. His high-drag, blunt-nose design not only made possible the development of an intercontinental ballistic missile (ICBM) within a few years, but paved the way for manned spacecraft with its new structures and materials.

The blunt-nose concept was just that—a concept. Years of design work lay ahead, along with materials experimentation, before a ballistic missile could enter the atmosphere without destruction, and before the recovery of a manned spacecraft would be practicable. NACA's role during this period was that of innovator, tester, and verifier. NACA's experimenters greatly enlarged the body of knowledge of thermodynamics and became well grounded in thermal protection, so that in time they were able to cope with the heating loads to be encountered in manned space flight.

Within NACA itself there was intense rivalry as to the best approach to space experiments. The Langley Center's Pilot-less Aircraft Research Division, working out of Wallops Island, was convinced that its method of using rocket-launched models was the best way to acquire information on heating loads, heat transfer, heat-resistant materials, and the behavior of bodies entering the atmosphere. At Ames, however, there was an equally firm conviction that wind tunnels and ballistic ranges were the most reliable tools for hypersonic research. It was along this line that Alfred E. Eggers, Jr., in 1958, developed an atmospheric entry simulator, which provided the equivalent of 100,000 feet of thickening atmosphere. Along with high-temperature jets at Langley and Lewis, the rocket tests at Wallops Island, the Army's Jupiter C shots from Cape Canaveral* in Florida, and other experimental methods, data were accumulated that later pointed toward ablation (the scaling off of successive layers) as the best method for protecting the interior of re-entry bodies.

Although NACA's official focus was on missile warhead development, this activity, concerned as it was with re-entry heating, was an obvious prerequisite to manned space flight, and there were pioneers in NACA who soon sensed the potential for manned space exploration, now beginning to look feasible, as military rocketry provided new propulsion means.

Since the military was developing the rocketry—albeit for missile purposes—it was logical that the first proposals for a U.S. space program should originate within the armed services. In 1945, the Navy's Bureau of Aeronautics set up a Committee for Evaluating the Feasibility of Space Rocketry. Their studies led the Navy in 1946 to propose to the Joint Research and Development Board that a small satellite be placed in orbit about the earth. The proposal was rejected on the ground of "insufficient military requirement." (Lest this summary decision come as a surprise, it must be said that in the military there is seldom a requirement until the capability exists—then requirements pop up after capability has been acquired like mushrooms after a spring rain. The reason for this is primarily budgetary—to admit to a requirement would lay the Defense Department open to claims for funding. That is why, for example, there had been no "military requirement" for a supersonic transport [SST], although it does not take too much imagination to foresee that when such craft are available the military will find ways to use them.)

---

* Renamed Cape Kennedy in 1964. See note on page 100.

In April, 1947, the Air Force–sponsored Project RAND found that earth satellites were technically feasible, and for several years thereafter the various services were permitted to pursue studies in this area. In June, 1954, a group of rocket specialists agreed that a satellite should go up as soon as possible for military and prestige reasons, even though the available booster rockets would permit only a small scientific payload with minimum instrumentation. Two months later the Army and Navy service chiefs concerned authorized the development of a joint Army-Navy satellite program using the Redstone boosters to be designated Project Orbiter. At the same time the Naval Research Laboratory was working with high-altitude research rockets and felt certain that a combination of these could launch a satellite for atmospheric research. It was this configuration—dubbed Vanguard—which eventually carried the burden of the first United States attempt to enter the space age. Although the Air Force also had a satellite proposal, it was based on using an ICBM as a booster. This, at the time, was an unfortunate choice; since the United States lagged in the missile race with the U.S.S.R., any space mission was considered "diversionary" and could not be supported since it would interfere with the development of the ICBM, which was then considered deserving of the highest national priority.

The voices of the space enthusiasts would not be stilled, however. Within the scientific community James Van Allen of the University of Iowa had proposed an earth satellite experiment at the 1948 meeting of the International Union of Geodesy and Geophysics. Later other international scientific unions, including the International Scientific Radio Union, in which Lloyd V. Berkener played a leading part, urged that satellites be used to expand upon the isolated findings of research rockets with respect to the properties of the ionosphere, upon which depended so much of the then existing earthbound radio communications.

Matters came to a head in October, 1954, when the international scientific community agreed to hold an International Geophysical Year (IGY) from July 1, 1957, through December 31, 1958, in order to observe a period of maximum sunspot activity. This was a scientific undertaking sponsored by the prestigious International Council of Scientific Unions and was designed to promote a broad, worldwide investigation of the earth-sun relationship by taking precise measurements around the globe and in the atmosphere at the same instant of time. The idea of orbiting a small earth satellite as part of the IGY stemmed from various sources, including a 1953 proposal of the American Rocket Society.

PROJECT VANGUARD

The proposal for a small, scientific earth satellite was formally put to President Eisenhower by the director of the National Science Foundation in March, 1955. Immediately the question was raised as to whether this would interfere with the ballistic missile efforts, which were just then getting under way. When the White House turned to the Defense Department for comment on the proposal, the response was that the project would not delay major defense programs and should proceed on a noninterference basis. And so in April, 1955, the decision was made to have the Defense Department proceed with a small scientific satellite to be launched under IGY auspices, but not to interfere with military rockets. This aspect of the policy decision proved fatal to U.S. hopes to win the race for the first entry into space. Especially since Vanguard—the Navy entry—had yet to be developed, while the Army's entry—the Redstone—was ready to go. Thus the separation of the scientific mission from the military hardware and an across-the-board defense economy drive led to a low-priority status for the IGY satellite within the defense structure.

The decision did not go through without struggle, however. The Army in particular fought to get the satellite project approved, and when it was disapproved, the Army kept on working with the Redstone, developing a nose cone and spare vehicles just in case the Navy project failed. As Vanguard lagged in its schedule, time and again the option of using the Redstone was turned down on the grounds that to use the Redstone would embarrass the Navy and upset the delicate balance of agreements among the armed services and the scientists.

There was considerable concern at high levels lest the Soviet Union make its announcement of its own intentions ahead of the United States and thus win "game points" in the propaganda battle of the cold war. Considerable attention was given to the coordination of the U.S. announcement so that it would be released simultaneously by the IGY Secretariat in Brussels and by the White House in Washington. The United States won the battle of the announcements—by twenty-four hours —its plan being made public on July 29, 1955, one day ahead of the Soviets.

No recital of the manner in which the U.S. Government organized itself to enter into the space age would be complete without some attention to the role of the U.S.S.R. in providing the spur to achievement that the United States seemed to need so badly.

It was not that the U.S. ballistic missile program of the 1950's had been barren of either managerial or engineering achievements. Although there were breakthroughs made, history shows that:

> The Soviet Union on August 26, 1957, successfully launched over its full design range a "super longdistance intercontinental multi-stage ballistic rocket."

> On October 4, 1957, the Soviets, apparently using the same ICBM, pushed into orbit the world's first artificial earth satellite, with an instrument payload of 184 pounds, called Sputnik.

A month later the Soviets put into a high elliptical orbit an instrumented capsule weighing some 1,120 pounds, containing a dog named Laika.

At the time the sole U.S. entry into this race was a Vanguard test satellite, with a three-pound payload, and it was still inert on its test stand at Cape Canaveral.

An atmosphere of disappointment, bafflement, and outrage was created through the highest levels of government by the Soviet achievements. The success of Sputnik reverberated through the halls of Washington like bells of doom. The hard, unpalatable fact was that the Soviets were first with the ICBM. They were first in space with heavy payloads, and the United States was short of its often proclaimed goal to keep ahead of, or at least abreast of, Soviet weaponry.

It was this latent fear of Soviet military superiority that caused such deep concern in the Eisenhower Administration. Bureaucratic delays, proliferation of committees, divided responsibilities, interservice rivalry, sacrificial attachment to a balanced budget, excessive waste and duplication, even for a crash program—these were some of the criticisms made by knowledgeable scientists, politicians, military specialists, and contractors against the Defense Department during the Truman and Eisenhower administrations. From 1953 to 1957, the Defense Department had seen over eleven major organizational changes pertaining directly to the missile program.

In the Aftermath of Sputnik

Within NACA the position of the space enthusiasts was greatly strengthened by the success of Sputnik. Although the agency was spending almost half of its budget on such space-related activities as nose cone research and flight at the inner edge of space, the amount was relatively small—less than $35 million out of a total of $80 million. It was apparent that the agency was at a crossroads. On one hand, if NACA continued to concentrate solely on aeronautical research, it would lose many of its best employees to whatever agency would emerge with the nation's space program; on the other, if NACA did take on space research, radical and far-reaching changes would have to be made. Sentiment within the agency among the younger employees below the middle management level was so overwhelmingly in favor of NACA's moving into the space field that Director Hugh L. Dryden felt justified in preparing a paper entitled, "A National Research Program for Space Technology," later called the Dryden Plan.

In an attempt to preserve the best of the old while permitting transition into the new, the plan did not call for the establishment of a new agency. Instead it proposed a space effort based on the cooperation of existing organizations—NACA, the Department of Defense, and the National Science Foundation. NACA would expand its space research program by enlarging its contract research program. Large-scale flight associated with military requirements would be under the Department of Defense with NACA providing the technical support. The National Science Foundation and the National Academy of Sciences would be responsible for planning the experiments to be conducted by the private scientific community.

Given the tempo of events, it was clear that unless NACA moved rapidly and adroitly it might very well be overwhelmed by the clamor for new solutions to old problems. NACA's key Committee on Aerodynamics held one of its periodic meetings on board the carrier *Forrestal* off the coast of Florida on November 18–20, 1957. Among the twenty-two representatives of industry, military, and the academic community, a consensus emerged that NACA should "act now to avoid being ruled out of space flight research . . . increased emphasis should be placed on the research of the problems of true space flight over extended periods of time." The committee called for "an aggressive program . . . for increased NACA participation in upper atmosphere and space research."

Two days later the Main Committee of NACA voted to establish a Special Committee on Space Technology, with H. Guyford Stevers, Dean of the Massachusetts Institute of Technology, as chairman. This was the first NACA committee ever to be concerned solely with space matters. Its role was "to survey the whole problem of space technology from the point of view of needed research and development and advise NACA" on action it should take.

NACA's Director Dryden, James H. Doolittle, chairman of the Main Committee, and John F. Victory, NACA's first employee and now its executive secretary, agreed that NACA should seek to extend its traditional pre-eminence as an aeronautical research organization into the more complex realm of astronautics. This could continue NACA's traditional function as planner, innovator, tester, and data-gatherer for the Defense Department and the missile and aircraft industry. If any larger role came to NACA, it would have to be thrust upon it—for there was to be no public campaign for any enlarged ambitions.

In keeping with this strategy, the Main Committee at its regular meeting of January 16, 1958, resolved to support the Dryden Plan in that any national space undertaking should combine the talents and facilities of the Defense Department, NACA, the National Academy of Sciences, and the National Science Foundation—in other words, the pattern of Project Vanguard would be retained. NACA would provide research and technical assistance, and the military would contract with industry for hardware development. As will be seen, nothing could have been less appealing to the mood of Congress, who, in the final analysis, would have the last word.

While this was the official position, the NACA third-echelon managers—those upon whose shoulders would fall in large measure the future management of any new agency—

were more outspokenly in favor of NACA's moving boldly into the space field. At a dinner held on December 18, 1957, these sentiments were made clear to both NACA Director Dryden and Committee Chairman Doolittle.

The space-oriented engineers from Langley and Lewis Research Centers felt that the agency should leave behind its historic preoccupation with research and expand into systems development and flight operations. In so doing, it would plunge into the competitive world of large contracts, full-scale flight operations, and the high-powered, show business world of public relations. In effect, it would assume the leadership of a broad-based national space program having as one of its principal objectives the demonstration of the feasibility of manned space flight.

The concept of a new civilian agency to lead the United States into the space age was also backed by the President's Science Advisory Committee, which specifically recommended that such an organization be built around NACA. The committee's recommendation was taken up by the President's Science Adviser, Dr. James R. Killian, with the Budget Bureau and the Advisory Committee on Government Reorganization with the intention of providing a definitive solution. They found the proposal to build a new civilian space agency on the NACA structure appealing for the following reasons:

- The agency had a large research staff and technical facilities;
- It already had moved into space research and if not allowed to move further its future would be in doubt;
- NACA had a long history of cooperation with the Department of Defense and was still staunchly civilian in outlook;
- It had a nucleus of space-competent young scientists and engineers who had been attracted by freedom of research opportunities;
- The agency had $300 million worth of research facilities—the best in the world for aerodynamic research and strong hyper-

sonic and space-related competence; and
* It had a reputation for fiscal integrity and effective money management, which had earned the respect of congressional appropriations committees.

The Administration's proposals were whipped into draft legislation and circulated within the government on March 26, 1958, with a request for comment by March 31. This by any normal standards was an extremely tight schedule for agency responses in any depth—especially from the Defense Department with its three military services and the Joint Chiefs of Staff, where a ten-day rule was in force to develop a coordinated viewpoint. Given the five-day deadline by the White House, the Defense General Counsel allowed the armed services and the Joint Chiefs a bare twenty-four hours in which to make comment. Since a quick reading seemed to imply that the new bill merely extended the military's past relationships to the new agency and since there seemed to be nothing in the draft that would inhibit the Defense Department from pursuing its own space missions, there was no formal objection raised to sending the bill to Congress. This was done on April 2, which led the then Majority Leader of the Senate, Lyndon B. Johnson, to remark that the draft had been "whizzed through the Pentagon on a motorcycle."

There were those in Congress and elsewhere who felt that NACA's administrative conservatism made it unsuitable to lead the nation into a bold new effort designed to wrest the space lead from the Soviets. NACA's habit of turning back to the Treasury unspent cash each year seemed to be the very antithesis of the management needed to gear up to a much larger level of exploration. There was also a view strongly held within the military and shared by their congressional supporters, that since the Soviet space effort was a threat to U.S. security, the military should lead the countereffort. With the U.S. missile program still in uncertain status, there were powerful voices opposing a civilian orientation for the new space agency.

It was against this background that the issue was sent to Capitol Hill, where an angered Congress would bring it to the attention of the American public.

II

The Creation of NASA

By the time the Eisenhower Administration's somewhat reluctant proposals for legislation creating a new civilian space agency arrived on Capitol Hill, Congress was already at work, busily attempting to stamp its own imprint on both the scope of the national space effort and its institutional framework.

Starting in January, 1958, a spate of bills had been introduced, each providing its own solution to the problems raised by the Sputniks. One bill, introduced by Senator Clinton P. Anderson, the powerful chairman of the Joint Committee on Atomic Energy, simply proposed that the law be amended to give the Atomic Energy Commission (AEC) a major portion of responsibility for the nation's space program. Not only was the White House alarmed by this proposal, but Congress was jolted as well.

Congress suddenly became aware that its time-honored system of standing committees would be hard put to deal with the legislative aspects of the newly emerging space program. For example, proposals on satellites that could observe the earth, either for weather or reconnaissance, could fall within the jurisdiction of the committees on Armed Services, Interstate and Foreign Commerce, Foreign Relations, Government Operations, or the Joint Committee on Atomic Energy. Clearly the lines of authority had to be straightened out or the legislative process would be hopelessly snarled. The solution in the Senate was to select the thirteen chairmen and ranking minority members of the important standing committees as members of a Special Committee on Space and Astronautics. Its chairman was the Majority Leader of the Senate, Lyndon B. Johnson. The House of Representatives achieved a similar solution by appointing thirteen members whose permanent committee assignments reflected their interests in space and related military or scientific subjects, with Majority Leader John W. McCormack as chairman.

Because its legislative hearing process had begun shortly after the Soviets had launched their dog-carrying satellite in November, 1957, the Senate was further along in its enlightenment than the House. The relationship between the Soviet satellites and a military threat to the United States had not been lost on the Senate Armed Services Committee, and its Preparedness Investigating Subcommittee, chaired by Lyndon Johnson, had taken statements from seventy witnesses and had interviewed two hundred more. The testimony of military, scientific, industrial, and government leaders running to 2,313 pages prompted the committee to urge that the United States put forth a major effort designed to ensure its pre-eminence in defense and space.

The House, on the other hand, had been immersed in hearings linked to the scientific aspects of space, and the membership of its special committee was more civilian-oriented. In fact, its chairman, the venerable Speaker of the House Sam Rayburn, was known for his persistent advocacy of a department of science within the executive branch, and it was to be expected that he would continue to press this view.

LEGISLATING A NEW AGENCY

It was through these layers of legislative preferences that the Eisenhower Administration's proposals began to filter. To make sure that space efforts would move ahead at reasonable speed while Congress pondered the future, the Administration on February 12, 1958, authorized the Secretary of Defense to engage in advanced research and development projects designated by the President and allocated $100 million in supplemental funds for the remainder of the fiscal year ending July, 1958.

Some writers have viewed the legislative process on Capitol Hill as a sort of tourney-at-arms ritual with champions jousting on the floor of the legislative chambers—useful as a sort of shorthand description of what took place in the development of the National Aeronautics and Space Act of 1958. In one corner of the field were the Defense enthusiasts being groomed by the Senate, and in the other were the civilian-scientific NACA champions sponsored by the House. In Defense's favor was its record of actual space accomplishment. Explorer I, which had been successfully launched on January 31, 1958, with a 31-pound payload, was the first U.S. satellite, and on March 17, the elegantly engineered but lightweight Vanguard had put a 3-pound payload into an elliptical trajectory that was expected to keep the satellite aloft for from 200 to 1,000 years. Explorer II was an 18½-pound payload fired into orbit nine days later. The Department of Defense had the booster rockets—the Jupiters and the Atlases. Although plagued with turbopump problems, these were the only likely workhorse vehicles for any U.S. space program. Defense had the firing ranges—at Cape Canaveral on the East Coast and Point Arguello on the West Coast. It had the money—some $100 million in the Advanced Research Projects Agency program. Given these advantages, the Pentagon felt that the legislation offered by the executive branch promised little more than a massive giveaway of Defense Department programs to a fledgling, untried civilian space agency, which might or might not carry out the military's requirements, depending on its own judgment as to where resources of money, men, and machines might best be allocated.

Although the Department of Defense (DOD) had been given only the minimum amount of time to respond to the Administration bill before it left the White House for Capitol Hill, the months of hearings provided opportunities for each element within the Department to ventilate its displeasure with the proposed legislation. In this effort its chief spokesman was Roy Johnson, the administrator of the Advanced Research Projects Agency (ARPA), who stated on May 5, 1958, that

> ... the legislation setting up a civilian group should not be so worded that it may be construed to mean that the military uses of space are to be limited by a civilian agency . . . for example if DOD decides that it is militarily desirable to program for putting man into space it should not have to justify this activity to this civilian agency.

Roy Johnson argued that the DOD should be free to operate in any field of space that seemed interesting without any prior approval by another agency and concluded by saying that he didn't know why there was any reason at all for a National Aeronautics and Space Administration, since the National Advisory Committee for Aeronautics (NACA), left as it was, was fully capable of pursuing nonmilitary space research. If, however, there was to be a NASA, then he proposed that the language of the bill be amended to provide that "insofar as such [space] activities may be peculiar to, or primarily associated with, weapons systems of military operations, in the case of which activity, the DOD will be responsible."

While the Defense Department's supporters in the Senate applauded this suggestion, the House leaders feared military domination over the new agency, and this new warning did little to reduce their concern. They were especially mindful of an admonition by such members of the Rocket and Satellite Research Panel of the National Academy of Sciences as Dr. James Van Allen, who earlier had pointed out:

The military services are basically operating agencies, not research ones. The research talent of any branch of the military services is almost inevitably turned toward helping meet short-term limited objectives. Such a point of view would assure the failure of a National Space Establishment in its broad mission which is truly a national one, far beyond the mission of any one of the services, or the Department of Defense taken as a whole.

Congress was not only concerned with military-civilian relationships, but with problems and issues of a scientific, economic, administrative, political, and international nature. Analyses by legislative experts showed that the Administration's bill either lacked or had no clear provisions for such essentials as congressional oversight and control, international cooperation, patents, indemnification for damages, limitations of liability, conflict of interest, ceilings on salaries, relations with the Atomic Energy Commission (AEC), formal liaison committee mechanisms, or over-all policy determination and coordination.

Another issue that concerned Congress was openness of information. In the Defense Department and the Atomic Energy Commission information could be released only if specifically authorized. In the new space agency scientists especially wanted a high degree of openness, with all information made public unless specifically prohibited.

Patents were another area in which outside pressures and interests were brought into sharp focus. The House members felt that a patent policy should be created along the lines of that prescribed by the Atomic Energy Act, which provided for government control of patents resulting from research paid for by the government. In the Senate, however, there was a split along doctrinaire lines. The antimonopoly and small business groups in that body went along with the House, but the more powerful chairmen who were closely allied to business interests paid heed to the pleadings of the American Patent Law Association. This group espoused the

corporate viewpoint, which felt that the Defense example of
existing patent rights in the research organizations should
prevail, regardless of the fact that the government paid for
the research, on the theory that the profits from such inventions were part of the incentives for industry to bid on defense
contracts and, in effect, kept the net costs down. In the
end there was a compromise, with the NASA Administrator
authorized to waive the government's rights if he deemed it
to be in the public interest.

Competition between the Defense Department and the proposed space agency for both men and material was another
source of concern. The Secretary of the Navy, Garrison
Norton, looked upon NASA's contracting authority as potential competition with the military for major aircraft and missile procurement, which, in his view, would lead to increased
costs and duplication of effort. So too the prospect of another
government agency's vying for skilled scientists and engineers
was also not pleasing to those who were concerned with ensuring the primacy of the DOD space effort.

Another source of contention in the legislative arena was
from the disparate efforts of the various agencies involved—
not only the embryonic NASA, but the existing departments and agencies—DOD, AEC, and the National Science
Foundation, to say nothing of the State Department, the
Commerce Department's Weather Bureau, the Federal Aviation Administration, and even the Federal Communications
Commission.

The Senate's legislative specialists felt that the overlap between the proposed civilian agency and the Department of
Defense might best be handled by a National Aeronautics
and Space Council to be chaired by the President, with members from the departments and agencies most concerned with
space and from the general public. The House favored the
establishment of a congressional liaison committee to handle
problems arising from this overlap.

Lyndon Johnson was one of the senators who favored establishing a nine-member National Aeronautics and Space Council, to advise the President directly and to be chaired by him. There were negotiations between the White House and the Senate on this point—with James R. Killian, the President's Science Adviser, taking the position that the Senate proposal was an affront to the President. (From the bureaucratic standpoint, the National Aeronautics and Space Council was anathema to the President's Science Advisers, who looked upon it as a rival for the President's attention.) This position was also taken by Lee A. DuBridge, who in the fiscal year 1971 budget hearing told the House Appropriations Subcommittee that the work done by the proposed council's staff of twenty could be taken over by the Office of Science and Technology with the addition of a "few" people. At any rate, Lyndon Johnson was adamant on the issue of the council, and, as it turned out, was to become its chairman as Vice-President in 1961, after a change in the law.

From the perspective of the President, however, there was something to be said for Eisenhower's reluctance to approve a new council, although the reasons were not brought forth until some two years later by an adviser to John F. Kennedy, Richard E. Neustadt, professor of government at Columbia University. In an address to the 1960 Annual Meeting of the American Political Science Association, Professor Neustadt listed as first among the problems of the President the chronic inability of interagency machinery to live up to expectations in the formulation and coordination of policy. He suggested that what was wrong was not the mechanism but the expectations. He felt that the machinery was being asked to do what it was generally incapable of doing—to develop bold and farsighted plans and turn them into prompt, effective action. Making plans and taking action, he pointed out, were the province of men within the departments, not men in between departments. Interagency committees, Neustadt perceived, were a type of legislative forum that could publicize, inform, debate, review, adjust, and authenticate but could neither initiate nor operate save on the lowest common denominator of agreement. Neustadt believed that it was futile to expect more of such a committee, and he concluded that, in approaching this issue, "one might suppose that the first step might be a change of expectations."

Although the Administration had agreed to changes in the bill it had originally excluded from consideration—an acknowledged separate role for the military in space and the establishment of a policy-level interagency board chaired by the President—there were still matters of difference between the House and Senate versions of the bill that called for reconciliation. The House version was passed on June 2, 1958, and the Senate version on June 16, but reconciliation did not take place for another month. After an almost complete breakdown in communications between the Senate and House committees, both houses agreed to a conference version July 16, and the President signed the bill on July 29, 1958.

The legislative process had hammered out a statute that provided for a national space program, with mechanisms for adjudicating the claims of the Defense Department and NASA via the National Aeronautics and Space Council and the President. It proposed a space program reaching far beyond anything originally conceived by the scientific community's approach to the global, synoptic measurement concepts of the International Geophysical Year and envisioned instead a program that would involve the United States deeply in utilizing space for the "benefit of all mankind," at the same time stressing the strengthening of national security objectives in space.

Although there were some expectations that Hugh L. Dryden, head of NACA, would become the Administrator of NASA, Congress was restive at the prospect of having a veteran career employee become the head of an agency charged with a dynamic new mission that called for bold vision and a capacity to think in substantial monetary terms.

In his testimony at the hearings on the National Aeronautics and Space Act, Dryden had identified three objectives on which he said work would begin soon after the establishment of NASA. One was to fly a satellite carrying an astronomical telescope with a television transmitter to send the pictures back to earth; the second was to develop rocket engines of 1 million pounds thrust, more powerful than those required for an intercontinental ballistic missile; the third was to develop manned spacecraft. Work on manned spacecraft, he said, would proceed cautiously. "I for one would be extremely reluctant to send men into space until their craft have been sufficiently proved to give them a much better than 50-50 chance to survive."

As far as it went, there was little to quarrel with in any of the foregoing. Then Dryden commented on a proposal made by Wernher von Braun and other Army witnesses to place a manned spacecraft atop a Redstone missile and launch it in a ballistic trajectory of several hundred miles. "To my mind," said Dryden, "such a flight has about the same technical value as the circus stunt of shooting a young lady from a cannon."

This statement raised an outcry, and Dryden was forced to explain: "This simple experiment . . . gives you a little scientific information at a great deal of cost. It may be justified as part of a very comprehensive program. . . . It might be that this is the place to begin."

His gaffe could not be rectified, and in the end, after a wide search, President Dwight Eisenhower named Thomas Keith Glennan the first Administrator of NASA. Glennan, president of Case Institute of Technology for eleven years, had served in Washington for two years, 1950–52, as a member of the AEC and presumably knew his way around the congressional booby traps. Hugh Dryden was selected as deputy administrator. Both men were promptly confirmed by the Senate and assumed office on August 19.

SETTING THE PACE

With the passage of the National Aeronautics and Space Act, there was a major change in the relationship between the Defense Department and the old National Advisory Committee for Aeronautics. Whereas in prior years NACA had been a valuable support agency fulfilling military research requirements, now NASA, elevated into the big league of government departments and agencies, with major budgetary demands of its own yet to be formulated, loomed as a competitor for funds as well as for Presidential and public attention.

On September 30, 1958, a notice appeared, as required by law, in the *Federal Register*, that as of the close of that day's business NACA would cease to exist. The legal transition to NASA took place overnight. The effective transfer took much longer and was accomplished by additions of people, programs, and facilities from outside the cadre of wind tunnel regulars who were the backbone of NACA.

Starting with the old-line NACA with its somewhat old-fashioned ideas of conservative budgets and the turning back to the Treasury of unspent monies each year, it was necessary to establish an agency with a new operational mandate—get the country moving on space projects and re-establish confidence in the hitherto unchallenged belief that the United States was indeed a leading, if not *the* leading, technological nation.

For NACA, which had lived for most of its official life in the shadow cast by the military services, the change was traumatic. Few, if any, other governmental agencies grew like NASA, from an essentially laboratory orientation to an operational one; few agencies had been created by the transfer of as many units and programs of other departments and agencies. From the start NASA was confronted by urgent demands for results. It was necessary to begin short-term programs as well as to work toward practical applications of space flight, particularly in the areas of weather and communications, and also to nurture long-term technological developments looking ahead a decade or more.

When the work of organizing the new agency began, NASA had 7,866 employees in its Washington headquarters and field centers. Then the build-up began. On October 1, 1958, the President transferred to the new agency the responsibility for the Vanguard project, and over the next three months about 200 employees moved from the Naval Research Laboratory to NASA. Also transferred were several space projects begun earlier in the year by the Advanced Research Projects Agency, as well as money transfers that made the officials of that agency grow pale.

Two weeks later, on October 14, Glennan requested that President Eisenhower assign to NASA the Jet Propulsion Laboratory, operated under contract to the Army by the California Institute of Technology, and on December 3, the laboratory with its 2,400 employees was transferred. A similar proposal to transfer the Army Ballistic Missile Arsenal at Huntsville, Alabama, with the Wernher von Braun group, which had succeeded in putting Explorer I into space, was delayed for a year while the Army fought a losing battle to retain a military mission in space. In the end, 4,300 employees of the Development Operations Division at Huntsville were transferred to NASA, although a substantial number continued work on missile programs that the Army had started earlier.

Thus at its beginning the space agency brought together a staff of widely diverse talents and skills, transferring from the research-oriented NACA, the civilian units of the Army and the Navy, and the Army's university contractors as well as military personnel on detail to these contractors. Personnel were also recruited from private industry and universities. By the end of June, 1961, the NASA staff had grown to

17,741, or double the NACA original. Contracting activity grew at an even faster rate; by 1961, four dollars out of every five appropriated supported contract operations.

NASA did not rely solely on the acquisition route to growth. In August, 1958, two new facilities were authorized by Congress. The Robert H. Goddard Space Flight Center at Beltsville, Maryland, was named in memory of the U.S. rocket pioneer. It was here that most of the Vanguard personnel from the Naval Research Laboratory were assigned to develop the array of U.S. scientific satellite payloads. A second new facility was established at Wallops Island, Virginia, where NASA took over the former Chincoteague Air Training Station on the mainland as well as the array of island launching sites that were to become a Cape Canaveral in miniature.

SPACE EXPLORATION

The initial NASA headquarters organization consisted of two program offices, reflecting the fact that space operations were an addition to NACA's research role. One office was responsible for the nonproject research and technology programs and the administration of the former highly autonomous NACA field centers. The other was responsible for space flight programs and for the new installations.

When it was decided to transfer the Wernher von Braun group at Huntsville to NASA, a third program office—for launch vehicles and rocket engine development—was established. The existence of this separate office reflected the general opinion that the United States could never hope to catch up with the Soviet Union in space until it developed launch vehicles that were not tied to missile requirements but to space requirements. It is ironical but true that U.S. launch vehicle development was held to low thrust because of the efficiency of our nuclear warheads, which did not require so large a thrust. In fact, the United States refused to consider any missile rocket booster until it became evident that the hydrogen bomb breakthrough was going to be a success. The Soviets were willing to use old-fashioned fission weapons if necessary and built their giant boosters accordingly. Hence the United States was forced to plan for giant vehicles in the absence of any military payload requirement.

Among the first new programs begun by NASA was manned space flight. Although the Air Force Research and Development command had been studying the technical problems for many years, President Eisenhower assigned responsibility for the first manned satellite program to NASA shortly before he signed the National Aeronautics and Space Act. On October 1, 1958, a coordinating committee of NASA and Advanced Research Projects Agency officials agreed that the objectives of the project would be to achieve at the earliest possible date orbital flight and recovery of a manned satellite. To investigate the capabilities of man in this new environment Robert R. Gilruth, assistant director of the Langley Research Center, and thirty-four other employees who had been studying various aspects of manned flight in space formed the nucleus of the space task group, with the project name of Mercury.

Another early program decision was made partly in response to early Soviet moon probe successes. On January 2, 1959, the Soviets' Luna I became the first craft launched into interplanetary space. Luna II made the first lunar impact on September 12, 1959.

The fact that Luna coincided with U.S.S.R. Premier Nikita Khrushchev's visit to the United States for a summit meeting at Camp David with President Eisenhower merely exacerbated the problem of putting the space show on the road.

Since the Soviet achievements were clearly tied to their political objectives, there was pressure on the new agency to show that the United States had capabilities for lunar and planetary probes. Accordingly, planning was begun for the exploration of interplanetary space, particularly the region between the earth and the two nearest planets—Venus, which is closer to the sun than the earth, and Mars, which is farther.

The orientation of the Jet Propulsion Laboratory toward lunar and planetary exploration became more definitive in 1958 when new responsibilities were assigned to it for conducting Ranger, Surveyor, and Mariner programs for exploring the surface of the moon and close-up investigations of the neighboring planets. Nine space vehicles were assigned to the laboratory's lunar missions from October, 1958, to December, 1960. As it happened none succeeded in reaching the moon, while the one interplanetary spacecraft, Pioneer V, launched March 11, 1960, went into a path around the sun between the orbits of the earth and Venus. Tracked and telemetered to a distance of 22,462,000 miles from earth, it set a long-distance communications record that went unchallenged for more than two and one-half years.

The group that had been transferred from the Naval Research Laboratory with the Vanguard program found itself concentrating on near-earth unmanned exploration at the Goddard Space Flight Center.

SPACE TECHNOLOGY

Meanwhile, the practical applications of space flight that required NASA's major attention were meteorology and communications. (Navigation satellites, because of their special utility for Polaris missile submarines, had been assigned to the Navy for development.)

In meteorology the TIROS (Television and Infra-Red Observation Satellite) program was carried forward by NASA in cooperation with the Weather Bureau and the military services. TIROS I, launched April 1, 1960, transmitted the first global cloud-cover pictures from space to meteorologists on earth and showed for the first time the details of the dynamic, swirling cloud formations that were to provide weather scientists with new data for forecasting and analysis. Since weather reporting was a traditional function of the government, there was no particular policy issue raised by the acquisition of such information by this new means. The same was not true of communications; in this country, in contrast to the rest of the world, communications for the most part remained the province of a government-regulated private monopoly.

The first demonstration of communications satellite potential was carried out by the military, with the pre-Christmas 1958 launching of an Atlas B booster containing a payload of taped holiday greetings to the world from President Eisenhower. Next was the NASA launching on August 12, 1960, of Echo I, a 100-foot balloon used to relay voice and television signals over intercontinental distances. Immediately the question arose as to how to make the best use of the satellite's potential for world communications. The demand for global communications was increasing in the United States at a rate of 15 per cent per year (as measured by the growth of overseas telephone calls), and there were comparable demands in the offing for transmission of data, written messages, and still pictures, as well as a large potential for television.

In the fall of 1960, American Telephone and Telegraph (AT&T) raised the question with Administrator Glennan as to whether NASA could provide rockets and launch services at cost, in order that AT&T might conduct research on the establishment of commercial space communications services. What AT&T had in mind was a medium-altitude satellite that would transmit signals to a ground antenna—a big horn shaped like great-grandma's ear trumpet, set up at Andover, Maine. In light of today's technology, such devices of the 1950's seem like charming antiques.

The pros and cons of the AT&T proposal were numerous; however, the Eisenhower Administration hoped to play a major role in space exploration and so the AT&T request was approved, as were NASA proposals to take the lead, within the executive branch, in demonstrating the commercial feasibility of space communications.

In addition to space exploration and applications of space technology, NASA's longer-range activities came into focus. The Senate Preparedness Investigating Subcommittee, mindful of the need to compete effectively in space with the Soviets, had recommended in 1957 the development of a million-pound thrust rocket—five times more powerful than the rockets used in the ballistic missile program. Two approaches were under way. One called for a cluster of eight liquid-fueled engines of the size then in existence to develop a total thrust of 1.5 million pounds. The other called for a new single liquid-fueled engine of the same thrust. This concept had been under study by an Air Force contractor, North American Aviation Company, for several years. NASA had inherited the project when it came in October, 1958, and in December it let its first major contract with North American Aviation for the engine, called the F-1.

Other major programs undertaken during these early years involved the use of higher efficiencies of liquid hydrogen as a rocket fuel, with work carried out on the Centaur program under Huntsville (George C. Marshall Space Flight Center) supervision. Liquid hydrogen was chosen as the propellant for the upper stages of the Saturn booster, and in early 1960 development was begun on a 200,000-pound thrust booster, called the J-2.

Other areas receiving attention at this time were the proposed nuclear rocket and various proposals for generating chemical and nuclear power in spacecraft.

In order to bring together in one coherent whole the various diverse activities that had been initiated, NASA prepared a ten-year plan, which was presented to Congress in 1960. The objective was to make certain that the various program components were mutually supportive and that powerful rockets would be available for increasingly more ambitious space flight missions. The plan, when unveiled, drew fire from two sources. The Eisenhower Administration considered it too ambitious; the Congress considered it too timid.

Congress was especially concerned because the plan considered that the first manned lunar landing lay beyond 1970, and that NASA's budget would reach a maximum of $1.6 billion in 1967. (Actually, peaking occurred in 1965 at $5.2 billion.) The House Space Committee complained, "NASA's ten-year space program is good as far as it goes, but it does not go far enough." Instead the committee recommended "a high priority program should be undertaken to place a manned expedition on the moon in this decade."

The second version of the plan was prepared with these criticisms in mind. Apollo was conceived as a second-generation spacecraft capable of carrying three men into earth orbit and circumlunar flight.

On the Edge of the New Frontier

In December, 1960, President Eisenhower received a report on manned space flight from his panel of the Science Advisory Committee. The costs of the Mercury-Apollo earth orbital and circumlunar program were estimated at $8 billion. The manned lunar landing was expected to cost $26 to $38 billion.

According to one of the staff people present at the review, the Chief Executive asked why a lunar landing program should be undertaken. On being told that it might be as important as Columbus's discovery of America, the President flared, "I'm not about to hock my jewels." The President's budget message to Congress in January, 1961, said the same thing in more formal terms. "Further testing and experimentation will be necessary to determine whether there are any valid scientific reasons for extending manned space flight beyond the Mercury program."

In the last budget of his Administration, President Eisenhower requested only $115 million for manned space flight, including Mercury. An additional $84 million was included for military astronautics within a $41.4 billion defense budget.

In retrospect, it seems only fair to say that in respect to the Eisenhower space program, there is little on record to dispute the view that budgetary considerations were of such overriding importance that little sense of urgency was permitted to show. Time and again the Administration asserted that the U.S. space program was adequate, that there was no "space race" with the Soviet Union and that Soviet achievements in no way implied a threat to national security.

The issue was debatable, and the Presidential election campaign of 1960 was powerfully influenced by the awareness that Sputnik had deeply hurt American pride, had caused a decline in U.S. prestige, and rightly or wrongly had indicated a lag in U.S. technology that opened up the suspicion of a gap in U.S. defenses. Democratic candidate Senator John F. Kennedy attacked the Eisenhower space record, while Republican Vice-President Richard M. Nixon defended it. The voters made the operational decision, and their verdict is history.

During its first two and one-half years NASA had grown far beyond the cloistered research-oriented laboratories of its NACA cadre. It had learned to operate with an annual budget in excess of a billion dollars and to cope with both a skeptical President and an impatient Congress. If the President's constraints had enforced a degree of order in the early development of the agency, congressional prodding caused it to raise its sights. It was against this background that the Kennedy Administration took over the direction of the government in 1961.

NASA at the end of the Eisenhower-Glennan era was a vastly different organization from the entity which had come into being twenty-eight months earlier. Its total employee complement had increased from less than 8,000 to over 16,000 (plus 2,500 contract employees working for the Jet Propulsion Laboratory). The NACA field installation system of three research laboratories and two flight stations had been expanded by three space flight development centers and several worldwide tracking networks. Facilities and working arrangements had also been established at the two major national rocket launching ranges—at Cape Canaveral and at Vandenberg Air Force Base, California. The annual budget had increased from $100 million to $1 billion, 85 per cent of which was spent by contract.

Administratively NASA had to deal with such problem-creating factors as:

- Rapid expansion of a new program through contracting procedures with industry and universities;
- Major recruiting for a greatly augmented staff;
- More efficient and responsible spending of large sums of public money;
- Interagency coordination—especially with the Defense Department and the Atomic Energy Commission;
- Organizing and conducting public information and education programs;
- Creating an environment conducive to scientific and technical creativity, while at the same time dealing with executive branch and congressional brush fires started, in the main, by leapfrogging Soviet space accomplishments.

Despite the effort to put together a successful management, the real test would come at the launch pads. While a good operation in Washington was necessary to sell and administer the program, it would be performance that would determine NASA's future. The questions lingering in 1958 were: Could we put a man in space? Could we land a man on the moon? What would the reaction be if we lost an astronaut?

III

The Organization of NASA

The transformation of NACA into NASA was as impressive
in its way as the transformation of the U.S. attitude toward
space after the first Russian Sputnik went into orbit—an attitude that changed overnight from almost complete indiffer-
ence to a burning desire to land a man on the moon. The
National Advisory Committee for Aeronautics was a relatively small research organization, unprepared to carry out a
program of the magnitude that the new National Aeronautics
and Space Administration would be asked to conduct. From
NACA's few hundred staffers, NASA would end up involving
millions of Americans in the manufacture, launching, and
follow-up of its specific programs; it would reach 34,000 in
manpower by 1966, with 400,000 contractor employees
working directly on NASA programs.

To carry out the mandate of Congress the National Aeronautics and Space Administration had to make immediate
changes from NACA. The new agency's role as defined in the
Space Act was to see:

that United States activities in space shall be devoted to peaceful
purposes for the benefit of mankind, and that such activities be

40

conducted so as to contribute materially to the expansion of
human knowledge of phenomena in the atmosphere and space,
the improvement of the usefulness, performance, speed, safety,
and efficiency of aeronautical and space vehicles, and the development and operation of vehicles capable of carrying instruments, equipment, supplies, and living organisms through space.

In addition, NASA was directed to conduct long-range
studies of the benefits, opportunities, and problems involved
in using aeronautics and space for peaceful and scientific
purposes; to preserve the role of the United States as a leader
in aeronautical and space science and technology, and in
applications to peaceful activities; to make available to defense agencies any discoveries of military value and significance; to cooperate with other nations in aeronautics and
space work; and to cooperate with other agencies to avoid
unnecessary duplication of effort, facilities, and equipment.

THE ADMINISTRATIVE CHANGEOVER

In fulfilling such a mission, the Space Act required that
NASA plan, direct, and conduct aeronautical and space activities, arrange for participation by the scientific community
in conducting measurements and observations, and provide for
the widest practicable and appropriate dissemination of the
results.

From the start, NASA's approach was to build a gov-
ernment-industry-university team to accomplish its goals. In
doing so, it had to become more than the technical resource
agency that NACA had been. Rather, it sought to become a
technical management organization, using the most advanced
communications techniques to direct and evaluate the performance of an interrelated network of government laboratories, industrial contractors, and university scientists.

Unlike NACA, NASA would have an Administrator, appointed by the President and confirmed by the Senate, who

would be in charge of the entire organization. While various department heads would contribute to decisions, it would be the Administrator who held the ultimate responsibility.

If NASA was to meet its congressional mandate, closer cooperation than had existed in NACA between the Washington staff and the field centers was necessary. The 8,000 field center employees under NACA were nearly independent; for NACA's Washington staff simply did not have the facilities to keep a tight rein on field center activity. While the independence of the various field centers plagued NASA in its first few years, the increased Washington staff soon allowed for close cooperation on a day-to-day basis and promoted a heretofore absent cooperation between it and the field centers. To further improve the headquarters–field centers relationship, NASA instituted the reorganizations of 1958, 1961, and 1963, which brought the centers closer to headquarters. The 450 members of NACA's five technical committees and twenty-three subcommittees no longer insulated the field centers from headquarters, and for the first time a clear two-way flow of information, necessary if NASA was to develop the tools to explore space, was available. In the most far-reaching organizational change, the field centers were put under control of the offices within NASA that made the most use of them. The Office of Manned Space Flight, for example, is in charge of the facilities at Cape Kennedy and the Office of Space Science is responsible for the Jet Propulsion Laboratory.

From its inception, NASA's leadership followed a policy of building and maintaining an exceptionally strong technical competence within its own laboratories. In part this was a natural outgrowth of the legacy left by NACA, which had achieved an international reputation for aeronautical research competence, and in part it was the reasoned position of NASA administrators, who felt that government representatives rather than contractors must make the basic determination of what is to be done with public funds. A good share of the nation's creative and managerial talent would now have to be recruited and retained. This would result in a career staff, capable of accepting full responsibility for hardware work done outside of NASA and numerous and competent enough to ensure effective contractor performance. NASA thus became a prototype of a management organization that builds its competence on a national rather than a local or parochial level.

THE EARLY YEARS

During the early years, the key word at NASA was "flexibility." Many old-time NACA employees were called upon to re-educate themselves in order to keep up with the changing character of research needs or to move into the new jobs where their experience and skills were urgently needed. Engineers who had been doing research on the operating structure of aircraft often found themselves dealing with problems of vehicles intended to fly in outer space, where unconventional forces had to be mastered. Men who had been working on theoretical research problems were suddenly coping with the fast-paced decision-making world of project management.

NASA's ability to manage the space program, especially the defense-aerospace sector which was responsible for furnishing so much of the hardware and sophisticated electronics required for both space and missiles, was heavily dependent upon American industry for its effectiveness in this specialized area where knowledge and experience were at a premium. In the defense-missile area alone, there were only a few contractors capable of the highly complex development, fabrication, techniques, materials, and new types of equipment that the space program required.

Just as NASA had to find ways to work with the industrial sector, it also had to find effective ways to involve the universities in the space program without becoming a competitor for the highly qualified and high-priced scientific and engineering talent that was needed to fulfill the universities' basic educational and research tasks.

The principal challenge to management skills, however, continued to grow in the manned space flight area. Here the key issue was keeping management informed of current difficulties in the vast, expanding program. As the Apollo 204 fire* on January 27, 1967, was later to show, keeping the contractor management informed was critical, for, without a complete understanding of all the technical relationships involved in a project, lives could indeed be lost.

The Apollo 204 fire at the Kennedy Space Center and the subsequent report of the review board, together with other internal evaluations by NASA officials, resulted in measures designed to prevent the recurrence of such disasters. From management's standpoint, it was vital to make certain that the self-policing features of NASA's organization and those elements of the system that were supposed to give advance warning of potential problems were functioning effectively for all levels of NASA management. It was with this in mind that in March, 1967, an Office of Organization and Management was established at headquarters, headed by an associate administrator. Its task was to bring together a number of offices that had been scattered throughout the organization in the 1963 decentralization process in order to provide a more integrated structure for effective decision-making. The new associate administrator of Organization and Management was made responsible for the improved performance of headquarters management. He was expected to develop and operate methods by which the agency could review and approve all major management actions and resources and to see that agency policies and practices were adhered to and

---

* This was the tragic fire in which three astronauts died inside their spacecraft on the launch pad at Cape Kennedy (formerly Cape Canaveral). See "A Tragedy and Its Aftermath" in Chapter VI.

that the requirements of Congress, the General Accounting Office, the Bureau of the Budget (now Office of Management and Budget), and the Civil Service Commission were understood throughout the organization.

In a similar move, the Office of the Assistant Administrator for Special Contracts Negotiation and Review was established within the new Office of Organization and Management to give special attention to procurement actions designated by the Administrator as significant enough to warrant continuing review and cognizance of one of NASA's senior officials. While this might have been construed as a loss of confidence in the system, which after all had worked well until the Apollo 204 fire, the facts of the review plainly indicated that improvements were vital in order to prevent a future tragedy. While NASA had been careful, manned space flight called for a new definition of the word "care," and special measures had to be taken to check and recheck details.

CENTRAL PLANNING SYSTEM

Another important milestone in the evolution of NASA's management system was effected by Dr. Homer E. Newell, who, following the departure of Deputy Administrator Robert C. Seamans, rose to the revived position of associate administrator. In this new role, Newell had the responsibility to study the pace, direction, and organization of the space program in the light of the completion of the manned lunar landing phase of the Apollo program. To bring to bear the most perceptive professional judgments, Associate Administrator Newell organized a central planning system to spell out the options available to the Administrator and to the President. Within this system, there arose a disciplined planning approach, using steering, coordinating, and working groups led by senior managers and scientists from both headquarters and the field centers. The system, it was hoped, would overcome the organizational barriers and break down some of the compartmentalization of functions, as well as eliminate competition and duplication of effort.

Another management innovation under Associate Administrator Newell was an effort to draw NASA's senior officials into a management council that would meet weekly to discuss various agency-wide policy problems and bring their expertise to bear on emerging program and operating problems.

NASA TODAY

The greatest administrative difference between NASA and its predecessor, NACA, was the elimination of NACA's Main Committee in favor of a single Administrator. From the beginning, NASA has always had a strong Administrator, a pattern set by James Webb, acting under the mandate of President John F. Kennedy. The influence of the Administrator of NASA is dependent both on the Administrator's personality and on the incumbent President's interest in space. During the Kennedy Administration, the Administrator had almost as much influence as a top Cabinet member. This influence decreased somewhat during the Johnson Administration and to an even greater extent under President Richard M. Nixon.

Although the Administrator is briefed by scientific and technical advisory committees from the nation's scientific and engineering communities, he is the sole and final point of decision within NASA. In his office proposals are drawn up and decisions for future programs are made. In addition to his duties of planning and decision-making, selecting the executive staff, and solving high-level problems relating to both hardware and personnel, the Administrator must also sell NASA to the American public and to Congress in the event of an unsympathetic Administration.

To assist the Administrator in his various tasks, a number

Organization Chart—National Aeronautics and Space Administration

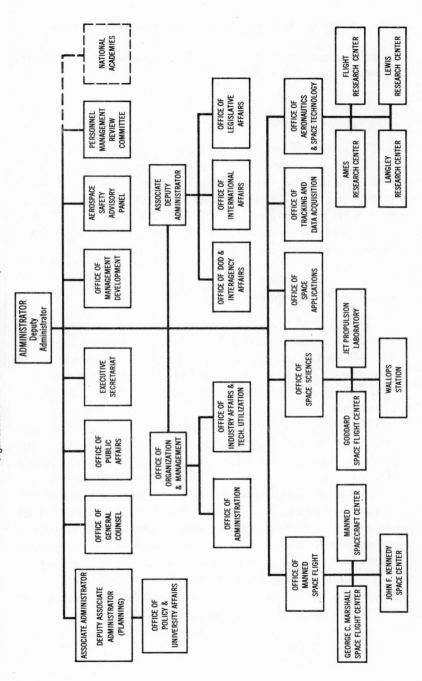

of offices lend support, several of which report directly to the Administrator (Chart I).

Office of the General Counsel

The Office of the General Counsel provides NASA with legal advice. While its functions are mundane (such as purchasing insurance policies for astronauts), they are necessary in a bureaucracy as complex as NASA. Grievances also fall within its jurisdiction—lawsuits against NASA for liability in the death of astronauts, for instance, and damage claims from falling satellites.

Office of Public Affairs

The Office of Public Affairs has numerous responsibilities outside the more traditional duties described in Chapter X. The Media Division of the office prepares audio and visual materials describing NASA and its functions and produces educational aids, booklets, and programs explaining NASA operations.

The Public Service Division answers mail inquiries, arranges for lunar rock displays and astronaut appearances, and prepares speeches for the Administrator and other NASA officials.

The Office of Public Affairs is responsible for a major educational program. Some thirty small trucks, equipped with exhibits, visit each of the fifty states each year to familiarize young people with the space program through illustrated briefings. NASA also sponsors a series of science fairs on the intermediate and high school level to stimulate interest in the program and the agency, as well as workshops designed to instruct science teachers in space technology.

Office of Policy and University Affairs

As mentioned earlier, NASA had to find a way to interest universities in the development of space science without seeming to steal the talent and skills that were needed by the educational and research divisions of the universities themselves. This is the responsibility of the Office of Policy and University Affairs, the universities' counterpart to the Office of Industry Affairs and Technology Utilization described in a later section in this chapter. NASA's approach here was to rely on the university community as its primary scientific resource and to devise ways to permit the needed skills to remain on the campus. No effort was made to bring all of the needed scientific talent into NASA field centers. Instead, university scientists were encouraged to become principal investigators in the development of scientific experiments to be flown in space while working within their university laboratories. In this way, they could involve their own faculty associates and graduate students wherever possible. The experiments would be scheduled by NASA, and the data obtained would be returned to the investigator for evaluation and for publication of research results. After a suitable waiting period, the basic data would be disseminated to other scientists for analysis.

For those scientists or engineers who could not involve themselves so deeply in NASA's experimental programs, a broad range of university grants was made available. In this way, individual or small group efforts in areas of interest to NASA could be funded without interfering with the individual research interests of the university faculty. This technique made friends for NASA and the national space effort in the halls of academe. Some critics contend that it also made biased witnesses out of scientists who testified each year in favor of the space program. Philip Abelson, editor of *Sci-*

ence, claimed that NASA-supported scientists in effect were "trained seals." (Most of the scientists who criticized the space program, it should be noted, were not beneficiaries of NASA's largesse.)

NASA has developed new forms of university relationships, such as the innovative Sustaining University Program for developing specialized manpower, not only for NASA but for national needs as a whole. In this program, universities were given support for three years' graduate training in space science and technology. Institutional grants were made directly to the institution, rather than to any particular project, to permit universities to be flexible in supporting scientific areas relevant—but not necessarily directly related—to space research, with the university making the judgment as to the merit of individual proposals and the allocation of resources. To help deal with a critical shortage of laboratory space, NASA offered relatively large grants to selected universities for construction of space science facilities.

In addition, NASA has encouraged more informal interchanges between itself and the university community. NASA employees have been sent to universities for upgrading and updating their technical experience, summer internships and summer institutes have been devised, and faculty fellowship programs instituted. Postdoctoral and adjunct teaching by NASA employees have involved thousands of people and have made a considerable mutual impact.

It has been NASA's intent that the universities develop the ability to put individual faculty members in a position to serve industry, their local communities, and society as a whole, in more effective ways than before. NASA encourages universities to band together in consortiums to foster cooperation among themselves, other research institutions, and the U.S. Government, for the advancement of space research.

Whether or not it was an unalloyed good for NASA to have directed university professors toward government and industrial research at the expense of personal relations with the student body remains to be seen. There is some question as to whether this move reinforced trends within the big universities to emphasize research tasks rather than teaching; it certainly brought many professors to Washington or international conferences when they might have been in the classroom.

On the other hand, NASA research offers an alternative to military research, which, in the new era of confrontation politics, arouses even more ire among restive student groups.

Management, Personnel, and Safety

The *Office of Management Development,* along with the *Personnel Management Review Committee,* is charged with providing the necessary manpower to run NASA and the necessary executive material to keep its standards high. The Personnel Management Review Committee reviews current employment situations and specific problems and acts as a "sensor" on the entire personnel situation within the agency. Together, the Office of Management Development and the committee handle cutbacks and increases in staff and offer personnel the opportunity to voice their ideas and, frequently, their protests.

The *Aerospace Safety Advisory Panel* is totally devoted to aerospace safety. If problems arise from a fire hazard at a field center or a tragedy on a launch pad, this is the organization to which the Administrator turns for assistance. Its day-to-day goals are to improve safety in aerospace activities, from fabrication to flight operation.

MANAGEMENT OPERATIONS

The mid-level of the NASA organization chart is the "housekeeping" level. The *Office of Organization and Man-*

agement, already described, is the center of the NASA bureaucracy. It is here that the decisions of the Administrator
are translated into employee assignments and agency policy.
Within this all-important office contracts are let, programs
are written, and congressional proposals are changed from
planning ideas into actual projects. The two major components of this office are the *Office of Administration* and the
Office of Industry Affairs and Technology Utilization.

On the same level as the Office of Organization and Management, an associate deputy administrator oversees the functions of three offices that affect NASA's operations in vital
ways: The *Office of DOD and Interagency Affairs* (see Chapter VIII) handles relations with the Department of Defense
and the rest of the federal establishment. The *Office of International Affairs* (see Chapter IX) conducts NASA's extensive
international space program, assisting in exchanges of information with other nations. The *Office of Legislative Affairs*
(see Chapter VII) is responsible for producing legislative
presentations to Congress and keeping Congress satisfied concerning NASA activities.

Office of Administration

The Office of Administration is primarily concerned with
coordinating all program and field center budgets and preparing the presentation of the budget to Congress in cooperation with the Office of Legislative Affairs after its approval
by the White House. While the Office of Administration is
tucked far away in the bureaucracy of NASA, its power is
undeniable. It is here that the budget experts squeeze dollars
from one area to save a program in another area. Priorities
are not sorted here, but the realities of NASA economics often
are.

Office of Industry Affairs and Technology Utilization

The Office of Industry Affairs and Technology Utilization, second of the two organizational units under the Office of Organization and Management, keeps the vital flow of contracts, cooperation, and program objectives moving with regard to the industrial section. It coordinates NASA programs with industry. "Technology Utilization" refers to the widest distribution and use by industry of knowledge gained from NASA research and programs. This function of the Office of Industry Affairs and Technology Utilization is discussed in Chapter XII.

To understand the magnitude of the involvement of the aerospace industry in the program, one need only to remember that, when NASA was at the heights of preparation for the Apollo manned lunar landing program, nearly half a million American workers in thousands of businesses were involved—from the 73,000 employees at North American Rockwell to the six-man circuit-board shop that had subcontracted something from another subcontractor. The Office of Industry Affairs and Technology Utilization makes certain that contracts are adhered to and that NASA policy and goals are maintained.

Industry faced a problem in responding to the new space challenge. Companies specializing in aircraft, missiles, electronics, and instrumentation had to make individual corporate decisions whether or not to compete for new business generated by the space program. NASA let industry know what its program needs were in a variety of ways—through contract statements of work, industry conferences, bidders' conferences, and discussion with industry managers. A number of decisions faced NASA concerning the way in which procurements were to be packaged—whether NASA would compete with the Department of Defense for the same materials and suppliers, and whether smaller companies should be used.

As it turned out, it was not always possible to develop precise designs for the hardware needed for the operational phase of the emerging space programs. There were too many variables for anyone to be able to say with certainty: "This is what we want you to build, and this is what you can plan on building. Now, what is your price?" Thus, because of the risks and unknowns of space research, the fixed-price contract was often found to be unworkable, and the more flexible "cost-plus" forms of contract were necessary. Incentive contracts were devised to achieve cost savings, to penalize poor performance, and to reward high performance and reliability.

In order to give the widest geographical distribution to federal research funds, NASA has developed a contract clause to be used in all research and development contracts over $500,000 and subcontracts of $100,000 or over. This clause requires contractors to use their best efforts to solicit proposals from the broadest geographical area consistent with efficient performance and without impairment of effectiveness or increase in cost.

While industry was expected to work out the complex arrangements involving subcontractors and parts suppliers, sometimes numbering in the tens of thousands, NASA's policy was to be more than a silent partner in building up this national capability. It offered industry substantial help through government research and test facilities, which were open to any contractor, and the services of NASA's technical and management staffs were made available to contractors in handling the special techniques, materials, and equipment that the space program required.

NASA creates opportunities for small business to participate in its procurement program by maintaining a small business specialist at each of its centers; by setting aside certain competitions for small business concerns exclusively, including all construction, alteration, and repair in the $2,500 to $500,000 range; by publishing in the *Commerce Business*

Daily names and addresses of all business firms that have been invited to submit proposals on procurements of $100,-000 or more in order to give small business concerns opportunities to participate in larger prime contracts as subcontractors; and by requiring prime contractors to consider small business concerns as subcontractors and to report on the extent of this subcontracting.

Despite industry's rather remarkable record of delivering space hardware within budget and on time, NASA has long been concerned with industry's lack of interest in ballyhooing the program on its own. Many at NASA's Office of Industry Affairs and Technology Utilization expressed the belief that industry was simply "lazy" during the mid-1960's when funding was generous and there was work for all. Today, these people believe that the aerospace industry is reaping the harvest of that neglect. To facilitate the NASA-industry relationship, NASA has established a number of internal organizations and policies that have attempted to make the most of the contractor's role in the space program.

The *Inventions and Contributions Board,* made up of six or more headquarters staff members, was established in 1968. All members have a vote except the staff director. The board meets monthly and has two main functions. To stimulate and accelerate the use of benefits from the space program by the general public, the board has the power to waive NASA's patent rights to discoveries made by contractors in a NASA-funded program. The contractor has the right, under law, to ask the board for the patent waiver. The board reviews the petition for the waiver and recommends further action to the Administrator. To encourage individual employees to be innovative, the board gives monetary awards for useful ideas. This awards program is discussed in Chapter XII.

In addition, the board continually surveys the progress that NASA and industry are making in the commercial application of those inventions and discoveries. Suggestions from all over the world regarding the space program come to the board for evaluation. When, in the board's opinion, a suggestion deserves further evaluation, it is forwarded to experts at the NASA field centers.

The *Board of Contract Appeals* was established to handle contract appeals made to the NASA Administrator. The *Contract Adjustment Board* was created to act when special defense requirements call for a departure from normal procedure and in accordance with procedures for extraordinary contract adjustments.

MANPOWER AND PERSONNEL MANAGEMENT

NASA is more than boosters, spacecraft, laboratories, computers, and communication networks reaching billions of miles into the universe. As much as anything else, NASA is people, selected and trained to carry out its unique mission.

From the beginning, NASA tried to attract a large number of highly qualified and experienced individuals who would be able to operate effectively with a minimum of organizational or policy guidance. Thanks to the Space Act of 1958, NASA enjoyed the advantage of special authority to employ a stipulated number of scientific, technical, and administrative personnel, without regard to the normal constraints of federal personnel regulations. In addition, the agency was permitted to employ a limited number of retired military personnel in a way which allowed them to work full-time and still retain their full retirement pay. Both of these provisions made available important reservoirs of talent and experience that might not otherwise have been available. As a side effect, the provision helped NASA build a clientele among the professional senior military, some of whom could look forward to postretirement careers with the agency, and some of whom already had close professional and social relationships with key NASA personnel.

The largest manpower contribution by far was that of the industry-university bases, supplemented by personnel resources of other agencies. Design, fabrication, test, and operation of space hardware systems was accomplished largely by industrial organizations.

NASA personnel, however, have always exercised full managerial control over all facets of a program, including those performed under contract. Its manpower strategy has been to use the field centers as institutional bases from which to build up managerial and technical competence, keeping in mind the need to de-emphasize programs as they reach their zenith and curve downward toward completion. This requires substantial readjustments in manpower within the contractor organizations rather than in the NASA part of the team, as the accompanying table shows.

NUMBERS OF NASA AND CONTRACTOR PERSONNEL
EMPLOYED ON NASA PROJECTS, 1960–71
(in round figures)

Fiscal Year	NASA Personnel	Contractor Personnel	Total
1960	10,000	37,000	48,000
1961	17,000	58,000	75,000
1962	22,000	116,000	138,000
1963	28,000	218,000	246,000
1964	32,000	347,000	379,000
1965	33,000	377,000	410,000
1966	34,000	360,000	394,000
1967	34,000	237,000	271,000
1968	33,000	235,000	268,000
1969	32,000	186,000	218,000
1970	31,000	135,000	166,000
1971	30,500	113,000	144,000

Budgeting, Accounting, and Procurement

In any government agency, the financial management system has to cope with legal requirements imposed by Congress in the authorization and appropriation bills, together with the practices set forth by the General Accounting Office, the Civil Service Commission, and other regulatory agencies. To meet these requirements, an agency has to develop budgeting, accounting, and financial reporting procedures. The financial system inherited by NASA from NACA was inadequate for NASA's larger and more complex programs.

NASA budgetary control was changed accordingly from the tight headquarters management of NACA to a more diffuse system of unit control. Line units would decide, after detailed advance planning, how they would spend the funds appropriated to them by Congress, pending headquarters' approval. Headquarters would step in only when departures from the plan exceeded prescribed limits. This new system reduced red tape and gave operating line units a larger spending latitude.

Since NASA is a research and development agency, most of the goods and services that it requires are unique and are not readily available from the commercial market place. To enable NASA to contract with individuals, corporations, and government agencies for products, ranging from multimillion-dollar launch vehicles to tiny high-quality electronic chips for spacecraft instrumentation, the Space Act granted procurement authority to NASA under the Armed Services Procurement Act of 1947. This Act provides that procurement can be effected not only by the traditional means of advertising for competitive bids, but also by negotiation—a technique developed during World War II.

In the case of competitive bidding, a standard contract is awarded to the lowest responsible and responsive bidder. When negotiation is used, a decision is arrived at by the evaluation of technical and management capabilities, and a supplier is selected to do the work. Intense negotiations are then begun to iron out the contract details. When both sides agree, the contract award is made.

In research and development contracting, the contract award is only the beginning of the over-all procurement process, since this type of contracting involves reviewing and evaluating the contractor's progress. NASA has to approve contractor actions that involve changes in costs, particularly when certain avenues of technical advance become blocked by, and do not yield to, available research means. In certain cases, contracts may have to be modified or perhaps terminated. All in all, contract administration is a team effort involving NASA's operating technicians and its procurement, safety, reporting, and security specialists.

To maintain consistency of auditing procedures of NASA and the Department of Defense, the Audit Division at NASA headquarters works in close liaison with the audit agencies of the three military services. As a result, much of the auditing of NASA contracts is done by Air Force, Navy, and Army audit agencies.

PROGRAM OFFICES AND FIELD CENTERS

The Office of Manned Space Flight, the Office of Space Science, the Office of Space Applications, the Office of Tracking and Data Acquisition, and the Office of Aeronautics and Space Technology encompass NASA's program effort. Ten field installations help to carry out the current NASA program under the headquarters cognizance of three of the above offices, as follows:

Office of Manned Space Flight
 George C. Marshall Space Flight Center, Huntsville, Alabama
 John F. Kennedy Space Center, Cape Kennedy, Florida
 Manned Spacecraft Center, Houston, Texas*

* In February, 1973, as this book went to press, the Manned Spacecraft Center was renamed the Lyndon B. Johnson Space Center in honor of the late President. It is referred to throughout this volume as the Manned Spacecraft Center.

Office of Space Science (formerly *Office of Space Science and Applications*)
   Goddard Space Flight Center, Greenbelt, Maryland
   Jet Propulsion Laboratory, Pasadena, California
   Wallops Station, Wallops Island, Virginia

Office of Aeronautics and Space Technology (formerly *Office of Advanced Research and Technology*)
   Ames Research Center, Moffett Field, California
   Flight Research Center, Edwards Air Force Base, California
   Langley Research Center, Hampton, Virginia
   Lewis Research Center, Cleveland, Ohio

Office of Manned Space Flight

The lion's share of NASA's budget has always gone to manned space flight. The Office of Manned Space Flight is responsible for making high-level proposals operational, for building and designing booster and spacecraft hardware, for launching recovery systems, training astronauts, and a host of other functions necessary to manned flight.

Within the Office of Manned Space Flight, program offices are established from the time a program is begun and continued not only until the program is completed but until all of the research data has been analyzed. The manned orbital Mercury and Gemini projects illustrate one of the reasons why the office makes huge demands on manpower. Although the projects were similar, different program offices were required because of differences in hardware, objectives, and timing. One program office must run the current program while another takes what knowledge it can from the current program and applies it to a future program. It has been the history of the Office of Manned Spaceflight to have to manage the end of a near-completed program, the current program, and perhaps one or two future programs all at the same time.

The Office of Manned Space Flight has three field installations of its own:

The *George C. Marshall Space Flight Center* is concerned with launch vehicle design and development. At this center, located outside of Huntsville, Alabama, stages of rockets are received from contractors and are tested and modified. The center also handles the integration of booster rockets and spacecraft and the design and integration of launch escape systems.

The *John F. Kennedy Space Center* at Cape Kennedy, Florida, is perhaps the most well-known NASA facility. Made up of launch complexes on a huge scale, it is responsible for the preparation of vehicles for launch, for final astronaut training, for preparation for emergency recovery, and for the destruction of aborting manned vehicles. The center also maintains facilities for large-scale unmanned launches for the Office of Space Science and shares some launch complexes with the Department of Defense in the unmanned area.

The Office of Manned Space Flight's real administrative center on the program level is the *Manned Spacecraft Center*. The center, located in the Houston, Texas, suburb of Clear Lake, looks much like a modern university. Here the astronaut corps lives and trains, and all technical planning and evaluation of manned flight is carried out.

When the words "Clear the tower" are heard from the firing room at Cape Kennedy during a manned launch, the responsibility for the flight switches to Mission Control in Houston. In a room filled with communications gear and computers, teams of experts working in round-the-clock shifts take over and monitor the launch through "return to earth." Launch timings, flight planning, flight crew assignments, delays, and midflight aborts are all decided by Mission Control.

The facilities at Houston and Cape Kennedy can be visited and toured by the general public. At the George C. Marshall

Space Flight Center a display featuring the Saturn V moon rocket is open to the public.

While the facilities of the Office of Manned Space Flight are separated administratively from other program offices, support from facilities administered by these offices is available to any division of NASA that requires it. Field center administration is divided along the lines of what office uses what facility the most, and in no way indicates exclusivity. Facilities are frequently shared.

Office of Space Science

The Office of Space Science is charged with the task of developing and launching a wide range of unmanned scientific instrument "packages." In addition, it prepares experiments for the Office of Manned Space Flight and, for other offices within NASA, provides scientific and technical support in areas of unmanned space flight and automated space payload packages.

It is the responsibility of the Office of Space Science to work with private organizations such as COMSAT (Communications Satellite Corporation) in the deployment of applications spacecraft. It also works closely with other nations in providing assistance in international space research. Prior to 1971, the Office of Space Science was the Office of Space Science and Applications, but to allow the office to pursue scientific investigations with greater vigor, the applications responsibility was assigned to a separate office.

The Office of Space Science does not have a huge manpower pool, its programs being on a smaller scale than those of the Office of Manned Space Flight. A more detailed account of its program will be found in Chapter IV.

The Office of Space Science is responsible for three independently operated field facilities:

The *Goddard Space Flight Center* in Greenbelt, Maryland, keeps track of spacecraft and other man-made objects in orbit and in flight through the solar system. Computers at Goddard convert the information transmitted by these objects into usable form. Scientists and technicians at the center edit these data on a daily basis and make them available to central data banks, so that NASA maintains an updated record of the exact status of all space traffic. A close working relationship has been established between Goddard and the ·Air Force's Strategic Air Command. The center's repository of data comprises the archives of our first years of space exploration and contains, as well, significant scientific findings about our own planet.

The *Jet Propulsion Laboratory* in Pasadena, California, is operated by the California Institute of Technology under contract to NASA and with NASA management and control. Spacecraft for the difficult and hazardous unmanned missions are designed, built, and tracked by the staff of this laboratory. Detailed descriptions of their projects will be found in Chapter IV.

The primary launch facility for the Office of Space Science is *Wallops Station* on Wallops Island in the Virginia tidelands. While this station is not as large as the installation at Cape Kennedy, thousands of small payloads have been launched from here over the years. Most international launches of sounding rockets and small satellites are done from here, also. The 70-foot Blue Scout rocket, using solid fuel, performs a seemingly infinite variety of services from Wallops. Payloads too large for Wallops are launched at Cape Kennedy or at West Coast military facilities made available to NASA.

Office of Space Applications

In 1971, to meet its challenge to increase the diffusion of space benefits into the daily lives of the American public,

NASA created the Office of Space Applications. Its position on NASA's organization charts puts it on the same level as the offices of Manned Space Flight, Space Science, Tracking and Data Acquisition, and Aeronautics and Space Technology. NASA believes that separate status will give the new office a closer working relationship with NASA research programs and will help emphasize the ever-increasing role of space applications.

The earth observation and communications programs, which will mean so much in the next decade, will be managed by the Office of Space Applications. In the words of NASA Administrator Thomas Fletcher:

> The application of space technology to solving problems here on earth is perhaps NASA's most important new thrust. I believe it appropriate to centralize into a single office in NASA headquarters all of the resources which we can muster to support space applications to earth.

Office of Tracking and Data Acquisition

Serving both manned and unmanned flight, the Office of Tracking and Data Acquisition works with all of NASA's field centers providing the communications facilities necessary to the implementation of a space program. The office also assists in the design of radio and television equipment. Without its technological expertise, the vivid color television we have enjoyed from the manned space program would have been impossible.

The Office of Tracking and Data Acquisition keeps contact with every man-made object in space. It is responsible for more than 1,000 manned or unmanned objects in orbit around the earth and the moon and cruising far out in deep space around the sun. Thanks to a globe-circling communications network, NASA can communicate with any of its active satellites and space probes at the flick of a switch, whether the spacecraft is on the moon, flying by Mars, or taking pictures of the weather around Australia.

Spacecraft-tracking involves much more than merely finding and following each spacecraft as it traces its own unique course through space. The location of the spacecraft must be accurately determined so that the scientific data it is acquiring can be matched to its position. Close monitoring of the spacecraft's path can register small perturbations which in themselves give valuable data about changes in gravity fields and atmospheric density.

To keep tabs on its many spacecraft, NASA operates four networks:

STADAN (Space Tracking and Data Acquisition Network)
   for tracking unmanned scientific and applications satellites;
SAON (Smithsonian Astrophysical Observatory Network)
   for precision tracking of satellites;
DSN (Deep-Space Network) for tracking lunar, planetary, and deep space probes; and
MSFN (Manned Space Flight Network).

The four networks are tied together with a common communications system called NASCOM. Using submarine cables, land lines, microwave links, and communications satellites, NASA can transmit data and voice messages around the earth in a fraction of a second. This high-speed communications system, plus an accurate timing system and a common geodetic base, make precise scientific measurements possible. Without these instruments, signals from satellites in orbit would be so much meaningless noise.

Office of Aeronautics and Space Technology

In the Office of Aeronautics and Space Technology problems encountered in man's exploration of space are overcome. In the four research centers it administers, a multitude of difficulties are studied—and, in some cases, first discovered. Practical benefits from space are also discovered at these centers and are put to the hard tests of earth applications. Center laboratories are concerned with both the manned and unmanned programs. The bell-shape of the first U.S. manned spacecraft, for example, originated not with the manufacturer, but with aeronautical scientists at the Langley Research Center in Hampton, Virginia.

The Office of Aeronautics and Space Technology is responsible for four large field centers:

The *Ames Research Center* at Moffett Field in California is responsible for laboratory in-flight research in space missions and aeronautics, including re-entry techniques, fundamental physics, materials, guidance and control methods, bioscience, and chemistry. The extensive aeronautical program is concerned with such areas as supersonic flight and Vertical/Short Takeoff and Landing aircraft. The space science effort at Ames revolves around the management of scientific probes and satellites and payloads for light experiments.

The *Flight Research Center* at Edwards Air Force Base, California, is concerned almost exclusively with the mechanics of flight within and outside the atmosphere. Both aircraft and spacecraft safety problems are examined and resolved here, and rocket planes and lifting-body devices are flight-tested.

The *Langley Research Center,* the oldest of the NASA field centers, is named after Samuel Pierpont Langley, whose primitive, turn-of-the-century aeronautical laboratory at the Smithsonian Institution on the Mall in Washington was a far cry from the center's modern facilities at Hampton, Virginia. Half the work at Langley is devoted to aeronautics. Its job is to improve the reliability of spacecraft and airplanes. The major technical areas at Langley are theoretical and experimental flight dynamics through the entire speed range. Flight mechanics, materials and structures, space mechanics, instrumentation, solid rocket propellant technology, and advanced hypersonic engine research are all studied at Langley.

Outside of Cleveland, Ohio, is the *Lewis Research Center*, whose main functions are power generation in space and aircraft, and rocket propulsion. Other areas of interest are materials and metallurgy, problems concerned with temperatures on spacecraft, chemical and nuclear rocketry, nuclear and electric power systems, advanced turbojet power plants, fuels, lubricants, and plasmas. Lewis Research Center has a field center of its own near Sandusky, Ohio—the Plum Brook Station—which maintains testing facilities for propulsion and nuclear research.

IV

Space Science

The eye of our largest telescope looks 11 trillion miles into space. To most of space, though, that telescope is blind, for far beyond its range there is more space, how much more can only be guessed, and thinking about it only heightens one's own sense of insignificance. Within the telescope's limited range, however, are a trillion galaxies, each containing several million stars. Our sun is merely one of the millions of stars in one of the smaller galaxies called the Milky Way. Man's way of thinking demands scale, and scale implies limits, but there are no limits to space.

Using robots made of sophisticated instruments, NASA's Office of Space Science proposes to reduce man's insignificance, if that is possible, and make him less ignorant of his universe. Since October, 1957, when Sputnik carried science into space, the United States has spent 25 cents of every space dollar on instrumented exploration of earth space and deep space. In NASA's words, the official job of the Office of Space Science is to "use automated spacecraft to make direct scientific measurements in space."

In the last fifteen years this office and its predecessor, the Office of Space Science and Applications, has launched more than three hundred spacecraft and has fired nearly two thousand sounding rockets into near-earth space. The magnetic field that surrounds our planet has been discovered and mapped, and the effects of solar radiation on our atmosphere and ionosphere have been studied. Spacecraft orbiting the earth have looked deeply into space and have recorded ultraviolet, infrared, gamma, and X-ray radiations from beyond our galaxy. Automated spacecraft have explored the solar system. We have mapped the moon and learned that other planets in the system are not at all like our own.

To launch its spacecraft, the Office of Space Science has developed a system of highly reliable, relatively uncomplicated launch vehicles with names like Scout, Thor, Atlas, Atlas-Centaur, and Titan III. Yet while the powered flight of those vehicles overshadows the delicate ascent of instrument-laden balloons and high-flying aircraft, these more conventional means of flight also play a major role in studies by this office. Even cloud-obstructed vision of earth-based telescopes is used in the space science program.

Spacecraft belonging to other government agencies, other nations, private companies, and universities, are also launched by the Office of Space Science, which sells the launch vehicle and the launch operation to the owner of the spacecraft. It is this service that made feasible two of our most important automated spacecraft types—communications and weather spacecraft (see Chapter XII).

Very much a service-oriented office, it provides launch facilities for the bulk of international programs and gives scientific support to experiments carried out in the manned program. Under the direction of the International Programs Office, the Office of Space Science has arranged for launches by institutions in cooperating countries, and has provided developmental support to institutions and nations cooperating in a joint launch. In addition, the office has put its field installations to work on problems that it may be able to help solve.

While only about 15 per cent of the Office of Space Science's budget is devoted to research, the foundation for all of its programs is its supporting research and technology program. The program objectives are to develop concepts and approaches for future flights, to develop the technology for future missions, to acquire the fundamental scientific knowledge to make the most of a future mission, and to supply this knowledge to other government agencies able to use it.

The Office of Space Science has been the grab bag office at NASA. The not-very-popular applications program had been left on the doorstep of the former Office of Space Science and Applications until officials realized that, if NASA was to survive the reordering of national priorities, it would have to delineate its contributions. Thus, in 1971, applications went off on its own to become the Office of Space Applications. Space medicine was also originally a misplaced function in the former Office of Space Science and Applications, and NASA officials appropriately transferred this responsibility to the Office of Manned Space Flight. What remains is a streamlined office, with a solid program that will, if past history is any barometer, produce remarkable discoveries in the 1970's despite the limitations of its budget. The office has withstood the decade in which attention was focused on manned flight and has made enormous contributions to science at moderate costs.

The main program functions of the Office of Space Science are divided into the physics program, the astronomy program, and the planetary exploration program.

Space Physics

When the first rockets and satellites broke through the atmospheric barrier, scientists discovered that outer space was not an empty vacuum. It seethed with particles from the solar system, stirred by the solar wind, with movement and interaction everywhere. The earth itself was found to exist within an elongated magnetic bottle that has a tail pointing away from the sun and extending beyond the orbit of the moon, which occasionally passes through it. The investigation of this area comes under the discipline of space physics, and most of the work is done by the Explorer-class satellites, some forty of which have been launched since the start of the space program. Their instruments have defined the Van Allen radiation belts, the magnetosphere, and the ionosphere.

In 1973 and 1975, three more atmospheric Explorers will be launched into orbit by the Office of Space Science. These 1,000-pound payloads will study the chemical actions of the earth's atmosphere. An on-board propulsion system will permit orbital changes so the satellites will be able to investigate the extremely low orbit area between 75 and 95 miles above the earth's surface. These satellites will cost $4 million with an over-all program cost of about $45 million.

Other work in space physics has been done by the 1,100-pound Orbiting Geophysical Observatories which carry twenty or more instruments making many simultaneous measurements. Recent emphasis is on mapping radiation zones, the ionosphere, and the atmosphere. One discovery made by such satellites was that the earth, the sun, and the eight planets of our solar system are passing through a huge cloud of hydrogen gas whose temperature approaches 10,000 degrees and whose speed is nearly 130,000 miles per hour.

Solar Physics

Solar physics, whose objective it is to obtain a more complete understanding of the sun's composition and behavior, has at its disposal the same vehicles that are used for space physics: rockets, satellites, and space probes. These vehicles carry instruments above the earth's atmosphere, where they can view the sun's ultraviolet and X-ray emissions as well as the abundant high-velocity particles that stream out of the sun at 100 miles per second.

To investigate solar disturbances that pulse through the interplanetary medium, the former Office of Space Science and Applications developed the Pioneer series of space probes, which have helped to chart the solar wind, solar plasma tongues, and the interplanetary magnetic field. NASA's major vehicle for solar studies, however, has been a series of Orbiting Solar Observatories. The first was relatively small, weighing about 500 pounds (later models have weighed as much as 1,400 pounds), and had a "sail" which pointed at the sun, and a spinning-wheel stabilizer section. Continuous observation of the sun yielded a means of predicting solar flares, useful in avoiding the hazard of solar flares during manned ventures into space.

Another important part of NASA's solar physics program is the Apollo Telescope Mount, which is managed within the Manned Space Flight Program as part of the Apollo Applications Program (see Chapter XIII).

An interplanetary monitoring platform program has been designed to further the study of the relationship between the sun, the moon, and the earth, by conducting a continuing study of the radiation environment between the three bodies. Two launches are planned for the early 1970's. The total cost of the program is expected to be about $75 million.

The High-Energy Astronomical Observatory is a future two-spacecraft project. Each observatory will weigh six tons and will study some of the most mysterious elements of the universe. Very energetic radiation from space, such as X-rays, gamma rays, and high-energy cosmic rays, will be studied. Previously, only sounding rockets have studied these possible X-ray sources. The first of these 30-foot satellites will be launched from Cape Kennedy in 1975 with a total program cost of from $180 million to $250 million.

SPACE ASTRONOMY

Space astronomy is another area of specialized scientific inquiry where the goal is to place instruments well above the earth's atmospheric barrier. While some space astronomy has been accomplished with sounding rockets and Explorer spacecraft, the difficulty in finding stellar targets and stabilizing the viewing instruments presented a major engineering challenge. The goal was to design an Orbiting Astronomical Observatory that would work. The engineering problems in designing the observatory spacecraft were overwhelming.

The first Orbiting Astronomical Observatory, conceived in the early days of NASA as a second-generation scientific satellite, involved greater technological advances than anyone had foreseen. The design contract was let in 1960. Major development problems included star tracking, and the computer control program alone carried some 300,000 instructions. The result was delay in launching the first observatory until 1966. A failure of the power supply on the second day after launch caused this first observatory to fail in its mission.

The second Orbiting Astronomical Observatory finally proved itself in December, 1968. It was equipped with an array of instruments for obtaining detailed measurements of stars and nebulae in the invisible ultraviolet region of the spectrum. Until radiation from the sun fogged most of its optics, the observatory returned more than 30 billion coded messages of what its eleven telescopes had seen in the heavens. Orbiting Astronomical Observatory III, a Stargazer spacecraft, was the heaviest and most expensive piece of unmanned space machinery ever built by the United States. Costing $100 million, it had a 38-inch telescope surrounded by 328,000 parts and weighed 4,800 pounds. Launched on November 30, 1970, it plunged back to earth in flames when its protective shroud failed to separate and its great weight kept the satellite from going into orbit.

Roughly 1,000 tons of meteoric dust sifts down through the earth's atmosphere every day. Where it all comes from no one knows. In fact, one of the big surprises in space physics has been the discovery of the possibility that the earth swings around the sun surrounded by a cloud of meteoric dust. The meteorites that fall to earth are millions of times larger than the particles in the earth's halo of dust.

Meteorites were ignored by science before the nineteenth century. Scientists considered it to be manifestly impossible for stones to fall from the sky. Only after the little French town of L'Aigle was bombarded by a volley of several thousands of such stones on April 26, 1803, did science finally admit the existence of meteorites.

Spaceship designers, from the earliest dreamers like Jules Verne to the engineers who plan modern manned spacecraft, have worried about these interplanetary projectiles puncturing the walls of their space vehicles. In the 1940's and 1950's, a number of engineers calculated the probability of a spaceship being perforated by a meteoroid. They based their estimates upon the number of meteor streaks seen high in the earth's atmosphere, and on studies made on meteoric dust obtained at high altitudes by rockets with flytrap devices. While these data were being evaluated, more were collected by spacecraft that carried instruments to measure micrometeorite impact as well as meteorite penetrating power. After more than ten years of investigation, the major conclusion was that any danger to astronauts, either in spacecraft or walking in space, is very small. Inquiry has now turned to the tiny dust particles which hover around the earth to determine whether they are fluffy particles or hard spheres like those found in deep sea sediments.

All of the great discoveries of space science—the Van Allen radiation belts, the earth's meteoric dust cloud, the magnetosphere, and the complexities of the sun-earth relationship—have given man a view of a universe that is far more dynamic than anything previously imagined.

Future Astronomy Programs

The Radio Astronomy Explorer satellite will be an orbiting antenna. Once in orbit, the 535-pound satellite will be 1,500 feet long and will monitor the often mysterious low-frequency radio signals that come from deep space. Measurement results will be free from earth interference. The satellite is scheduled to be launched into lunar orbit from Cape Kennedy in 1973. The total cost of the program is expected to be about $20 million.

The Small Astronomy Satellite will be a 400-pound Explorer-class satellite and will study the gamma and X-ray sources outside our galaxy. It will be launched by a Blue Scout rocket from the Italian launch platform San Marco off the coast of Kenya in the early 1970's. The total cost will be $40 million.

PLANETARY EXPLORATION

The planets of the solar system have always been a source of interest to man, and, as our closest neighbors in an otherwise inhospitable universe, have been looked upon as a potential source of life.

Mars

Mars is a particularly favorite target for astronomers' telescopes. Some observers have claimed that its surface is covered with a gridwork of artificial-looking lines so astonishingly straight that many believed them to be canals. When the first space probes took off for Mars, keen interest was aroused not only by the pro- and anti-life debate, but also by the controversy over the possibility of canals and what their existence would imply.

After three failures with earlier probes, NASA's Mariner

IV encountered Mars on July 15, 1965, after a flight of 207 days. The probe came within 6,200 miles of the planet and transmitted its findings back to earth, 135 million miles away. Close-ups of Mars looked like telescopic pictures of the moon. They showed a planet pockmarked by craters—perhaps 10,000—with diameters between 3 and 75 miles. The atmosphere was thin, so thin, in fact, that it offered little protection against lethal ultraviolet radiation from the sun.

From the evidence transmitted by Mariner IV, scientists concluded that Mars had neither canals nor life, although several linear features appeared in the photographs in regions where "canals" had been seen from earth. To informed viewers, the lines looked like well-weathered and pockmarked natural features—perhaps cracks in the planet's crust caused by meteoroid impacts. No signs of life were apparent, but similar photographs of the earth taken from satellites with even sharper details showed no conclusive signs of life on earth, either.

Mariners VI and VII, launched in 1969, were highly successful in obtaining new data, including some that pointed to the probability that the existence of even microbial life on Mars was less than had been previously supposed. It also appeared likely that Mars had never had an ocean. Terrain aspects of the planet, some featureless and some chaotic, were visible evidence of presently unknown surface phenomena. The heavily cratered polar caps seemed to be covered by a thin layer of ice consisting of a possible mixture of carbon dioxide and a small amount of water.

The highly successful Mariner IX probe continued to show Mars to be a very inhospitable place compared to the earth. The spacecraft mapped the planet in an amazing performance. Detailed photographs again looked much like the moon. Extremely high mountains and huge craters were typical features. The versatile spacecraft even gave us close-ups of a Martian moon that looked like jagged pieces of brown rock floating in space.

Further exploration of Mars is planned for 1975 and 1976 when Project Viking will soft-land instrument payloads on the planet. The spacecraft will have an automated orbiter and a Mars lander. Total weight will be 7,500 pounds, one of the largest unmanned flights that NASA has undertaken. After lift-off from Cape Kennedy aboard an Atlas/Centaur rocket, the spacecraft will travel 460 million miles. After going into orbit, the sterilized lander will detach itself and land, using a parachute and retro-rocket pack.

The scientific equipment on the orbiter will include television, water-vapor- and temperature-mapping instruments. The lander will feature two color television cameras and instruments to determine atmospheric composition and weather conditions, and will sample the Martian soil. By far the most expensive undertaking in the history of the Office of Space Science, the program is expected to cost $750 million.

Venus

Venus, shrouded in clouds and rotating once every 240 to 250 days in a retrograde motion opposite to that of all the other planets, is another priority target for scientific inquiry. With a surface temperature perhaps as high as 800° F.—which would give it lakes of liquid metals—Venus has, like Mars and the moon, been the objective of both U.S. and Soviet scientific spacecraft.

The first U.S. success in the quest for knowledge of Venus was achieved with Mariner II, launched on August 27, 1962. One hundred and nine days later, and 36 million miles from earth, it passed within 22,000 miles of the mystery planet. Microwave radiometers on the satellite confirmed the "hot planet" theory, with little change in temperature between the day and night sides. Five years later, in October, 1967, two probes flew past. One was NASA's Mariner V; the other was Venus 4, launched by the U.S.S.R. Their experiments were basically different, but there was a good deal of overlap, and, while the results did not concur exactly, they were generally noncontradictory. The probes found that Venus was a hot planet with a thick atmosphere of carbon dioxide, with a bizarre, superrefractive quality that traps electromagnetic waves entering at certain angles from the outside so that they cannot leave again.

Other Planetary Probes

The most far-reaching project planned by NASA and the Office of Space Science is the dual 570-pound Pioneer flight to Jupiter for a close-up look at a planet one thousand times bigger than the earth. The two-year trip to Jupiter will be strewn with obstacles ranging from the asteroid belt to Jupiter's radioactive field, 3,000 times more dangerous than that of the earth. Each spacecraft will be capable of carrying out thirteen separate experiments.

Using a nuclear generator for electric power, the twin spacecraft (separate launches, months apart) will spend a week in the vicinity of Jupiter. The $105 million program is the most important Office of Space Science program for the early 1970's.

Another project planned by the office is a 1,100-pound Mariner spacecraft that will engage in a flyby of Venus with a gravity assist to fly by Mercury in 1973 and 1974. Two cameras aboard the Mariner will send back detailed pictures showing the planets, while instruments will measure the weather and atmosphere of Venus and Mercury. The project will cost $120 million. Other future programs of the Office of Space Science are discussed in Chapter XIII.

COOPERATION WITH THE OFFICE OF MANNED
SPACE FLIGHT

No one in the Office of Space Science will pretend that competition for funds does not exist between it and the Office of Manned Space Flight, but personal bitterness is usually lacking.

Three programs were designed by the Office of Space Science to function in cooperation with the Apollo manned lunar landing effort of the Office of Manned Space Flight. The first of the programs, Ranger, was designed to give scientists a closer look at the moon and thus indirectly help the Apollo designers. The second, the Surveyor craft, was designed to soft-land on the moon, take samples, and survey the lunar terrain. The Lunar Orbiter was designed to map the moon.

Even before the Apollo moon landings became a high-priority national objective, the Ranger program was under way at the Jet Propulsion Laboratory to take photographs of the lunar surface and effect a hard landing on the moon.

Rangers VII and VIII, launched in 1964 and 1965, were flawless in their accomplishments. Scientists and the world at large were thrilled to see the thousands of photographs showing countless lunar craters of all sizes. Those pictures taken just before impact revealed details less than two feet apart. Such pictures gave scientists a better look at the lunar surface than would centuries of telescope-gazing. The accomplishments of Ranger IX, also launched in 1965, were even more prestigious than those of its predecessors in that the pictures transmitted to the Jet Propulsion Laboratory were instantaneously transmitted to the entire world.

The Lunar Orbiter, a second-generation spacecraft, was one of NASA's most successful projects. All five orbiters were launched and completed their lunar missions during the years 1966 and 1967, and their initial cost of $80 million remained on target with only minor exceptions. The hundreds of pictures taken by the orbiters covered the entire lunar surface. Parallel ridges and troughs were seen in the rough lunar uplands, new information was obtained on hitherto unsuspected fresh craters, and, most importantly, the Lunar Orbiters helped to certify five future manned landing sites.

Surveyor was NASA's most troublesome early problem child. Like Ranger, it was approved in the 1960's before the Apollo program. Its total cost was estimated to be $125 million for seven flights, but by 1965 the program was two and one-half years behind schedule, and its estimated total cost had tripled. Reviews were instituted at NASA headquarters in 1964, and a major reorganization followed. The Surveyor project staff rose from 100 to 500 in a few months. The contractor came under investigative scrutiny by the Jet Propulsion Laboratory, and a series of negotiations and changes were instituted to provide tighter control of the project.

The House Committee on NASA Oversight studied the difficulties surrounding the Surveyor program and concluded that NASA had not done sufficient groundwork for Surveyor at the project's start, that headquarters control over the laboratory should have started sooner, and that the laboratory was concentrating on Ranger and Mariner while leaving the contractor in sole charge of Surveyor. In all, the report was an unflattering comment on the much-vaunted government-university-industry partnership. However, when Surveyor I left Cape Kennedy on May 30, 1966, it surprised everyone by its perfect performance. It braked to a soft landing and sent back pictures of the lunar landscape. Of the seven shots from 1966 through 1968, only two failed to land and return data.

FIELD CENTER COOPERATION

The basis for survival of the Office of Space Science has been twofold: generating missions of scientific import that deserve funding and providing support services vital to the over-all health of the agency. The test of its ability in this regard is in the operation of the field centers, which provide the research and development information necessary to the implementation of any of the office's programs.

Soviet and U.S. Lunar Activities

The Soviet Union and the United States have always been in competition for the space spotlight. The Soviets showed an early interest in the moon and for many years seemed to be trying to be first with a manned lunar landing. As it turned out, they were the first to obtain a lunar sample from an unmanned spacecraft and return it to earth with Luna 16, in September, 1970. Luna 17, in November, 1970, landed an eight-wheeled robot on the moon. The size of a railroad hand-car, it propelled itself across the moon's surface, carrying radios, a television camera, an X-ray spectrometer to analyze the moon's soil, and an array of mirrors to reflect laser beams back to earth.

The two successful Soviet lunar satellites, coming at a time of budgetary stringency in the U.S. space program, spurred another round of the perennial debate over the merits of manned versus unmanned space activities. In support of the manned flights, NASA officials were quick to point out that the U.S. manned flights returned hundreds of pounds of materials, while the Soviet unmanned flight returned but three or four ounces. Congressional interest in the Soviet Luna achievements prompted Acting NASA Administrator George M. Low to summarize the official NASA view of the merits of manned versus unmanned systems:

The principal goal of Apollo was to establish and to demonstrate United States preeminence in space science and technology through a *manned* lunar landing. But Apollo did more than that: it also demonstrated that important scientific results can be attained in manned space flight. It is virtually impossible to conceive of practical unmanned systems that could accomplish many of the many important things done by our astronauts—the discovery of unexpected features of the moon, the careful selection and documentation of lunar samples, and the reporting of conditions on the moon other than those measured directly by instruments selected in advance. Unmanned robot systems approaching the capabilities of the astronauts would, through their complexity, tend to approach manned systems in cost without ever matching their capability.

One may, in my view, generalize from these remarks as follows: When the details of a space mission can be defined in advance and when the task to be performed is relatively straightforward, an unmanned system can best do the job.

MOON ROCKS

Since one of the major scientific expectations from the initial manned flights to the moon involved the collection of lunar materials, a special effort had to be made to analyze the lunar samples once they were brought to earth. This required the proper quarantine measures to ensure that no harm would come to either the lunar samples through contamination or to the earth environment by release of possible lunar organisms. To meet this need and ensure proper archiving and distribution of the priceless lunar samples, a multimillion-dollar Lunar Receiving Laboratory was established at the Manned Spacecraft Center. In order to insulate itself from the institutional and individual requests to work with the lunar samples, NASA asked the National Academy of Sciences to suggest a practical way in which either the Academy or a consortium of universities could take over the management of the laboratory.

The Academy's response was the Lunar Science Institute, which was built adjacent to the Manned Spacecraft Center to provide a university atmosphere for scientists wishing to have access to the unique facilities of the Lunar Receiving Laboratory, whose management it also assumed. Forty-eight universities were organized by the Academy into a consortium known as the Universities Space Research Association in a major effort to ensure enhanced communications between the nation's top researchers and the operating .personnel at the Manned Spacecraft Center.

NASA officials also had reason to be proud of the successful operation of the Automated Lunar Surface Experiment Package—the automated monitoring station that was left on the lunar surface.

BIOSCIENCE IN SPACE

No question relating to space meant more in the mid-1950's than the question of life on other planets. When Sputnik was announced, that question was moved far back in people's minds, but it was never forgotten. Now that the political implications of space in the cold war are no longer an issue, scientists are again asking if there is life elsewhere in the universe. NASA's Office of Space Science instituted a series of programs to try to find out. The Office of Space Science has become increasingly more concerned with space bioscience, thus adding another dimension to its contributions to the over-all NASA mission.

The office formerly had a biosatellite program, which ended after only a few flights. It told much about how life from earth develops in space but little about new or unfamiliar life forms. It instituted a bioscience program that had two primary objectives: 1) the detection and understanding of extraterrestrial life and 2) the effects of the space environment on terrestrial species. However, since space bioscience is closely related to space medicine, biotechnology, and human resources, these responsibilities were transferred to the Office of Manned Space Flight.

The investigation of the origins, development, and distribution of life in the universe comes under the discipline of exobiology. It involves the investigation of the development of complex organic compounds on the moon and the planets, which might give clues to prebiological evolution leading to the threshold of life, and studies of biological adaptation to learn about the capacity of living things to change to meet the challenge of different environments (total light or total darkness; a great variety of atmospheres, such as pure ammonia or methane; temperatures found near boiling volcanoes or freezing glaciers).

The search for organic matter on the surface of the moon is one of NASA's most exciting areas of investigation, if only to test new theories on the origin of life. Meteorites recovered in an uncontaminated condition might provide information on chemical and biological events in the far reaches of the universe. That is why such pains are taken in the Lunar Receiving Laboratory to preserve the integrity of lunar samples.

Even though Mars appears to be arid and lifeless, scientists and bioscientists feel that the Martian atmosphere is adequate for biological cycling. They consider the planets to be important, even if life is not found, since they may still provide clues to chemical evolution.

Other programs of concern to the bioscientist are planetary quarantine, space health applications, gravitational biology, biological clocks and rhythms, orientation and navigation, and terrestrial ecology. Research has been pursued in such areas as limiting the deposition of fat in the body, depressing body functions as protection against radiation and to enhance cancer treatment, learning how the body uses protein more effectively during certain hours, and designing procedures for the best use of the food that will have to be consumed on spacecraft in missions lasting several years.

Bioscience programs are closely coordinated with similar programs of the Office of Manned Space Flight and the Office of Space Applications. The role that space bioscience has played in the "new medicine" will be described in Chapter XII.

V

Americans in Orbit

On December 17, 1958, the fifty-fifth anniversary of the Wright brothers' first flight, Administrator T. Keith Glennan announced to the press that NASA's manned space satellite program would be called Project Mercury after the messenger Mercury of Grecian mythology. The project's goal would be to put an American in orbit around the earth and return him safely. He would fly in a funnel-shaped capsule the size of a telephone booth, after having been boosted into space by an Atlas D intercontinental ballistic missile. The name Atlas was appropriate for the booster in that the god Atlas was the grandfather of the messenger Mercury. The Atlas missile, however, did not take well to its role as a booster of NASA payloads, as illustrated by an early Atlas missile that achieved an altitude of three inches before dissolving into a spectacular fireball.

The years 1958 and 1959 were difficult ones for the Mercury people at Cape Canaveral. The Air Force personnel who ran the facility did not like civilians invading their roost, but, despite the disappointments and the Atlas failures, there was never any question that the United States was determined to put a man into space, if for no other reason than to save face internationally.

To competent professionals, the Atlas launch failures of 1958 and 1959 were necessary points on a learning curve. A lack of failures would have reflected a tempting of fate. As it was, the failure rate was about what an engineer could expect, considering the technology gap to be closed and the urgent pressures that were striving to close it.

As development of the large liquid-fueled rockets proceeded, the prospect of manned flight beyond the earth's atmosphere hinged more and more on the question of survivability of man in space. As propulsion and guidance problems were overcome, physiological and psychological unknowns became the major obstacles to success.

WEIGHTLESSNESS AND OTHER PROBLEMS

Because the National Advisory Committee for Astronautics had been concerned almost exclusively with techniques of flight within the atmosphere, research in medical problems of space flight had been the province of the military services and some civilian research organizations funded by the military. The U.S. Air Force considered space medicine as a further extension of aviation medicine and had undertaken most of the early studies into the psycho-physiological problems of extra-atmospheric flight. At first, flight physicians were almost unanimous in expressing their misgivings about the effect of weightlessness on man's physical and mental performance. Some feared that the body organs were so dependent on the earth's gravity that they would not function if deprived of this force. Others were concerned over the combined effects of acceleration, weightlessness, and heavy deceleration during atmospheric re-entry. Still others were worried about perception and equilibrium, fearing that the labyrinth of the inner ear would be so disturbed that it would not be able to function.

One basic difficulty regarding the study of weightlessness

TWO FAMOUS FIRSTS

Participants in the first meeting of the National Advisory Committee for Aeronautics, April 23, 1915. Represented were the War Department, Navy, Signal Corps, Bureau of Standards, Weather Bureau, and three universities.

Launch of America's first man in space, May 5, 1961. The Overseas Travel Order for Alan Shepard's fifteen-minute suborbital flight included the following:

TRAVEL BY REDSTONE ROCKET BOOSTED MERCURY SPACE CRAFT; U.S. MARINE CORPS HELICOPTER; U.S. NAVAL AIRCRAFT CARRIER AND AIRCRAFT. . . . THE USE OF A RENTAL VEHICLE IS AUTHORIZED IF ADVANTAGEOUS TO THE GOVERNMENT.

All photos on this and the following pages are from the National Aeronautics and Space Administration.

NASA's early years were marked by failures as well as successes. This Vanguard launch vehicle rose to 20,000 feet, then veered off course and broke apart, while attempting to put a small geodetic satellite in orbit on February 5, 1958.

John Glenn was the first U.S. astronaut to orbit the earth. *Below:* The rocket carrying Glenn in the Friendship 7 spacecraft lifts off from Cape Canaveral, Florida, February 20, 1962. (Cape Canaveral was renamed Cape Kennedy in 1964.)

Kennedy Space Center, Florida, today, showing the "rollout" of the Saturn IB rocket to be used to launch the Skylab orbital workshop crew.

Edward H. White II was the first American to walk in space. He is shown here on June 3, 1965, secured to his Gemini 4 space-craft by a 25-foot umbilical line and a 23-foot tether.

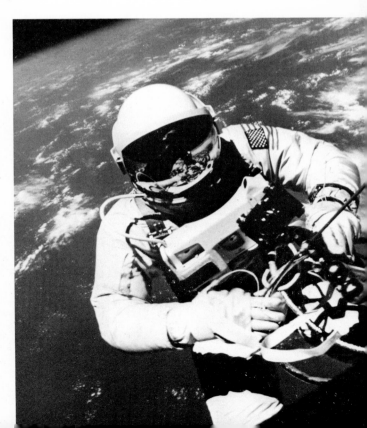

Above: Scientist-astronaut Harrison H. Schmitt and his Lunar Roving Vehicle traverse the desolate lunarscape during man's most recent trip to the moon, in December, 1972. *Below:* Schmitt examines a huge, split lunar boulder at the Taurus-Littrow landing site.

The first men to walk on the moon await helicopter pickup in the Pacific, July 24, 1969, as a pararescueman closes the hatch of their spacecraft.

Looking down on Apollo 17 a few seconds before a perfect Pacific splashdown, December 19, 1972.

Earthrise on the moon. It will be many years before an American witnesses such a sight again.

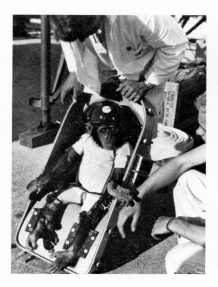

Before the first American was launched in space, in 1961, NASA's environmental-control and recovery systems were tested with chimpanzees.

As part of NASA's international program, the Italian San Marco satellite was launched on December 15, 1964, by a NASA-trained Italian crew.

An aerial view of a part of the NASA Manned Spacecraft Center, Houston, Texas. Shortly after the death of ex-President Johnson in 1973, the Center was renamed the Lyndon B. Johnson Space Center.

NASA's Mariner spacecraft was constructed to orbit Mars and send back pictures of the terrain. Four solar panels, attached as outriggers, give the 2,200-pound craft a span of 22 feet.

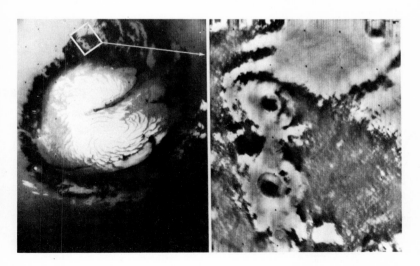

Left: Mariner 9's picture of Mars's north pole on October 12, 1972. The polar cap is about 620 miles across. *Right:* A high-resolution picture of the 90- by 125-mile area outlined in white at the base of the polar cap.

An artist's conception of a
space station. Each module
has a particular role—for
example, as crew quarters,
control center, or galley.

An aircraft of the future,
drawn automatically by a
computer from a numerical
description of a design
under study at NASA's
Langley Research Center.

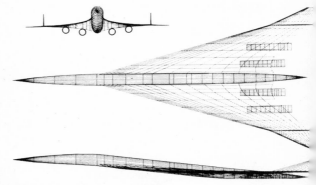

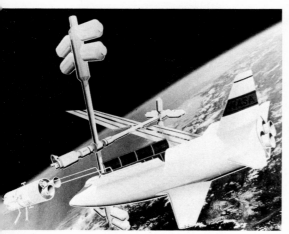

Sketch of the Space Shuttle
(right) transferring fuel to
a Space Tug *(left)*. The
modular space station in
the background would also
be supplied by the Shuttle.

was the impossibility of duplicating the exact conditions existing on earth. The X-15 rocket plane, which NACA had sponsored along with the Air Force and the Navy, was considered by many to be the penultimate step to manned flight, but its development was proceeding too slowly to shed much light on the immediate problem of weightlessness. By the fall of 1958, when the newly organized NASA began planning a Mercury manned satellite, only the Soviets had put live subjects into space orbits, and their dog Laika was the only living proof of survivability. By 1959, about a year after Project Mercury had gotten under way, the U.S. Air Force, by using aircraft trajectories, was able to report that "the majority of flying personnel enjoyed the exposure to subgravity in controlled experiments . . . [and] even longer periods of absolute weightlessness can be tolerated if the crew is properly conditioned and equipped."

Another perplexing problem was the effect on the human body of the heavy acceleration and deceleration forces called g-loads. Many fighter pilots in World War II had suffered pain and blurred vision from excessive g-loads during "redout," when blood pooled in the head during an outside loop, or "blackout," when the heart could not pump enough blood to the head as an airplane pulled out of a steep dive. Since a space mission would involve even higher g-loads, an astronaut would weigh several times what he normally did on earth, and a severe strain would be imposed on his body organs. Students of g-forces in the late 1950's tried various devices, such as nylon netting, multidirectional positioning, and water immersion, to expand human tolerance limits during high g-forces. These solutions were impractical, though, in the small spacecraft required by the thrust limitations of the U.S. boosters then in use. Because of these limitations, a small craft was the only feasible design for a U.S. manned satellite.

As it happened, the solution to this problem of body support did not come from biodynamicists but from practicing aerodynamicists in NACA's Pilotless Aircraft Research Division, where the space enthusiasts had worked out the design features of an extremely strong and lightweight couch made of fiberglass, which could be contoured to fit the body dimensions of any individual. In the spring of 1958, the results of various centrifuge tests showed that man could survive peak loads as high as 20 g's, using the lightweight couch. The trajectory for the planned manned satellite would theoretically expose the passenger to only 9 g's. NACA engineers working overtime on a manned orbital capsule were elated. It seemed that they finally had an effective anti-g device that was both small enough and light enough to fit into the one-ton capsule envisioned for the first U.S. manned space venture. But what they did not realize was that the body angles of the couch were more significant than its contoured support for protecting space pilots from sustained high forces. Thus, they had inadvertently made a major breakthrough.

The final element in the NACA/NASA campaign to minimize the effects of gravity build-ups was the use of experienced military test pilots. During the centrifuge experiments of the 1950's, pilots had consistently proven themselves capable of withstanding higher stress forces than nonpilots. The groundwork was thus laid for one of the most significant and at times controversial aspects of manned space flight: that it would remain for some time the exclusive province of experienced engineering test pilots.

A key question that had to be solved in the development of manned space flight was the precise role of man in the satellite—was he there to test the vehicle, or should the vehicle test him? Aviation engineering had from the beginning assumed that man was not only a passenger but was also an integral part of the machine which he controlled, using his power of decision in both expected and unexpected situations to ensure a margin of safety that could not be equaled by machines alone. In contrast, rocket technology had for the most part been concerned with missiles, in which automatic controls were the heart of the system ensuring target accuracy. If a missile failed, there was no need to save the payload. But when, in the Mercury program, man became the payload, an integration of the philosophies of aviation technology and rocketry was called for, and there was dispute over which of the two disciplines would have control of the operating spacecraft. Important elements in the civilian, scientific, and engineering community bore down heavily in favor of automation. According to John R. Pierce, the father of communication theory and communication satellites and research chief of Bell Telephone Laboratories, "All we need to louse things up completely is a skilled space pilot with his hands itching for the controls." On the other hand, the military, particularly the Air Force, and the missile industry held to the opinion that man was the essential payload and that his performance as a part of the system held the key to full utilization of the space environment.

NASA's initial decision was a cautious compromise. Since no one knew exactly how well man would take to space, the Mercury was designed for automatic flight, with man functioning predominantly as a passenger. From the cost-effectiveness basis alone, however, man's decision-making ability was irreplaceable.

NASA's compromise did not silence the debate over man versus machine control of spacecraft. Dr. Robert Jastrow, director of NASA's Institute for Space Studies, claimed that "it is cheaper, not dearer, to carry out scientific research on the moon by man rather than with robots. The short history of space flight is filled with examples of manned missions that would have failed without men aboard, and of unmanned missions that did fail for want of a fix that could have been supplied by men."

On the other hand, Dr. James Van Allen, the space scientist

who discovered the belt of radiation encircling the earth, strongly disagreed. Advising the United States to phase out its manned space programs, he said, "Maintenance of men in a spacecraft increases the cost of a given mission enormously and risks human life unnecessarily and in a conspicuous and dramatic way."

A NEW BREED OF HERO: THE ASTRONAUT

In an age of anti-heroes, the introduction of man into space provided the United States with a new type of hero—the astronaut. It was not until April 9, 1959, when the first seven astronauts were presented to the press, that the public began to exhibit pride in the national space program.

It was decided that these pioneers of space would be called astronauts, just as the pioneers of ballooning had been called aeronauts. The astronauts wore civilian clothes, and their previous roles as military test pilots were played down. Their public comments were restrained. They seemed to represent native Americans of average build and good looks. They were family men, college-educated as engineers, in excellent health, and professionally dedicated to flying advanced aircraft. Despite criticism that the selection of astronauts was unrepresentative in that no members of ethnic groups were included, the names of Carpenter, Cooper, Glenn, Grissom, Schirra, and Shepard were to become as familiar to the American public as the name of any famous actor, soldier, or athlete. The fame of the astronauts and public curiosity about every detail of their lives quickly exceeded any relevance to their earlier activities and flight mission assignments. Commercial competition for publicity and the pressure for political prestige in the space race whetted an insatiable curiosity about this new kind of celebrity so that at times it became difficult, if not impossible, to separate the astronauts' public personalities from their private lives.

Project Mercury achieved great public attention. Even before their skills were put to the test of space flight, the Mercury astronauts were lionized by both the press and a public anxious for reassurance that the United States had champions who would answer the challenge posed by the Soviet Union's early space successes.

Gradually, as experience increased, the man-versus-machine arguments became less strident. There was a shift from dependence upon automation to monitored automatic flight, with man's role becoming essentially that of a diagnostician, determining what was going on within the system. To reinforce the astronaut, the information he received was sent to the ground, where large banks of computers and systems specialists analyzed it and stood ready to supply more information to the astronaut if necessary. That is the essential reason for the large flight control rooms with their scores of specialists and display boards that tell whether the systems for which they are responsible are functioning as they were designed to function.

COMPETITION FROM THE SOVIETS

Although it was apparent that the Mercury manned space program was going to be the United States' primary effort to achieve space parity with the Russians, Mercury was still basically a research and development program with a host of technical problems, and its pace could not be forced. The Russians, despite their own technological problems, were forging ahead. On May 15, 1960, the Soviets orbited the first capsule large enough to hold a human passenger. Weighing over 10,000 pounds, the capsule failed four days after launch when its control system shot the capsule (containing a dummy astronaut) the wrong way for recovery. If there was any complacency over this mishap, it was short-lived, for on August 19 of that same year the Soviets orbited another large capsule, and on the following day they recovered two dogs from orbit.

While the Soviets were advancing, Mercury was suffering growing pains. Because it was a research and development program, designs and schedules had to absorb changes that sprang from increasing realization and understanding of space problems. Costs and time tables had to bend to improve quality and reliability. Care had to be taken to avoid so many "quick fixes" that a pyramid of unobtrusive changes could conceal the possibility of something going wrong.

Such was the setting when the second Mercury/Atlas test flight was launched into low clouds above Cape Canaveral on July 29, 1960. One minute after lift-off the missile exploded into tiny fragments. NASA headquarters took this failure in its stride and on the same day announced plans to follow Project Mercury with a manned space flight program called Apollo, a project planned to carry three men in either "sustained orbital or on circumlunar flight." Given the failure of the Mercury shot, this announcement seemed bold and visionary indeed, yet to the space engineers the failure merely reflected another point on the learning curve. They never doubted that lessons would be learned and that space flight would indeed be mastered.

The intense pressure to compete with Soviet successes took a heavy toll of the NASA launch team. Divorces, heart attacks, and a number of tragic suicides within the program are evidence of how seriously Mercury was being taken by those responsible for the program.

As Project Mercury stretched on into 1960 without much to show for millions of taxpayer dollars, criticism began to mount from both the public and the trade press. Some of the criticism was allied with the competitive Dynasoar program projected by the Defense Department, which, before it was canceled, also envisioned manned space flight with a maneuverable capsule to be recovered on land.

At NASA headquarters there was serious concern over how to answer public criticism. Officials pointed out that the contractor was working the equivalent of a 56-hour week, that 13,000 people were in direct support of the project, and that production was on a 7-day week, three shifts per day, while launch crews were working a 70-hour week.

Although the planners were philosophical, the disappointments continued. On November 9, 1960, a test designed to put the Mercury capsule through maximum dynamic pressure saw the disintegration of the rocket only sixteen seconds after lift-off. Twelve days later, a test with a Redstone booster achieved a 4-inch lift only to have the main rocket engines shut down and the escape tower take off, while the booster settled back on the pad.

The gap between the successful Soviet space flights with their heavy payloads and biological specimens and the U.S. flight qualification failures was worrisome to an American public concerned with the space race. In the three years since Sputnik, the Soviet Union and the United States had launched into space a total of 42 vehicles—38 earth satellites, 3 solar satellites, and 1 lunar probe. The box score in the space race showed 33 U.S. launchings and only 9 Soviet launchings, but with their 9, the Soviets had put 87,000 pounds into space as opposed to the U.S. total of 34,240 pounds. The Soviets had hit the moon, had photographed its dark side, and had recovered two dogs from orbital flight.

As the year 1960 drew to a close, the Soviets were experiencing failures also. Their December launch and recovery of two more dogs ended in cremation of the animals when the spacecraft burned up on re-entry from too shallow an orbit. Despite this setback, the Soviets announced, "We are on the threshold of manned space flight, and the first man in space will undoubtedly be a Soviet citizen."

The Soviet promise was made good on April 12, 1961, when Yuri Gagarin became the first man to complete a round-the-earth orbit. Although the flight did not have the impact of Sputnik I, many Americans were disappointed, including the U.S. astronauts who had hoped to be first, at least with a suborbital flight. That NASA still had a long way to go was amply demonstrated by the launch of a Mercury/Atlas on April 25, 1961, which contained an electronic mannequin. The spacecraft was destroyed by a range safety officer forty seconds after launch, when the inertial guidance system failed to pitch the vehicle toward the horizon. "The news will be worse before it is better, and it will be some time before we catch up," President Kennedy said on hearing of the Gagarin flight. The Mercury/Atlas disaster showed how true his prophecy was. As it happened, this was the last major flight failure in the Mercury program.

SUCCESS—SHEPARD, GRISSOM, AND GLENN

On May 5, 1961, Alan B. Shepard, Jr., took off from Cape Kennedy in a Mercury capsule above a Redstone booster, rose to an altitude of 116.5 miles, attained a maximum speed of 5,180 miles per hour, and landed 302 miles downrange from the Cape, after a flight of 15 minutes and 22 seconds. The flight was covered by all the media, and the whole world was able to share the excitement of Shepard's brief journey. For the first time, the maiden flight of a revolutionary manned vehicle, climaxing years of research and development, was open to public view. What most enhanced U.S. prestige was not the technical skill of the flight but the contrast between the open-door policy of the U.S. toward news coverage and the wall of secrecy that surrounded the more technically advanced Soviet program. From the standpoint of the cold war and the implied struggle for men's minds, which had been a central issue in U.S. post–World War II foreign policy, the most rewarding feature of the Shepard flight was worldwide comment, which concluded that the differences in the ways the United States and the Soviet Union handled their space programs reflected the basic differences between the two societies and their essential values, methods, and goals. The sense that the flight was a Western achievement was widely echoed throughout the free world, and the belief that the U.S. would make the scientific results of its space experiments available encouraged a sense of involvement and participation.

The flight of Astronaut Shepard gave the whole country a lift. It made the space program seem more immediate to the American public. Shepard, along with his fellow astronauts, was flown to the White House, where President Kennedy decorated him with NASA's Distinguished Service Medal.

In a duplicate of Shepard's ride, Virgil "Gus" Grissom climbed into Liberty Bell 7 and flew for 15 minutes and 37 seconds on July 21. After splashdown something went wrong with Grissom's hatch, and the capsule was lost. The rescue helicopter made a valiant attempt to recover the water-logged capsule, but the copter's red warning light, which had been on for a full minute while the capsule operation was in progress and before the astronaut had been picked up, indicated that it would be too dangerous to continue to try to save the capsule.

On May 25, 1961, in a special message to Congress, President Kennedy announced that the time was at hand "for this nation to take a clearly leading role in space achievement, which in many ways may hold the key to our future here on earth." He continued:

This nation should commit itself to achieving the goal, before this decade is out, of landing a man on the moon and returning him safely to earth. No single space project in this period will be more impressive to mankind or more important for the long-range exploration of space; and none will be so difficult or expensive to accomplish.

With the challenge laid out, and the deadline set, the nuts and bolts of the foundation for the effort would be Mercury. For the first time, what was known earlier as Project Astronaut was now part of a much bigger picture.

THE FIRST U.S. MANNED ORBITAL FLIGHT

Although the Russians had succeeded in orbiting Gherman S. Titov seventeen times for 25 hours and 18 minutes on August 6, 1961, the proposed flight of John Glenn was continually delayed. The United States was prepared to launch Glenn only after the chimpanzee Enos had flown a duplicate mission and survived 181 minutes of weightlessness and the searing re-entry. After Enos had successfully completed his flight, the press began to wonder if the United States would be ready to orbit a man in 1961. Newsmen began to file speculative stories on an early manned attempt when John Glenn moved into the special astronaut quarters at Cape Kennedy, but on December 7 it was officially announced that the flight would not take place until early 1962.

Delay after delay burdened the NASA Mercury team in January. At a news conference on February 14, President Kennedy indicated that he shared the disappointments of the unlucky space project and reaffirmed his faith in the Mercury team by saying that he would continue to abide by the judgment of the team. That judgment was vindicated on February 20, 1962, when Friendship 7, an Atlas 109 D, rocketed John Glenn into three orbits around the earth and returned him safely after a frightening few hours with a malfunctioning sensor. The United States could now be proud of its space endeavors.

After his successful flight, John Glenn spoke to Congress. The President, now dramatically tied to the future of space, listened with total fascination. In the White House rose garden after Glenn's speech, President Kennedy said, "We have a long way to go in this space race. But this is the new ocean, and I believe the United States must sail on it and be in a position second to none."

While the nation celebrated John Glenn's flight, NASA and the prime contractors for Mercury were already hard at work preparing Gemini, a spacecraft that astronaut Walter Schirra said "made Mercury look like a Model T."

AURORA 7

Model T or not, Mercury faced many more flights, beginning with the Aurora 7 flight of Scott Carpenter. Carpenter was preparing to fly a duplicate of Glenn's mission with some new experiments added. On May 24, 1962, Aurora 7 took off as 40 million Americans watched the spectacular event on television. The flight again proved the basic integrity of the Mercury/Atlas system, although it revealed some minor flaws in the capsule. The most noticeable deviation from Glenn's flight was that Carpenter landed several hundred miles off target because he was late in his retrofire sequence.

The lessons that had been learned in the early disappointments were beginning to pay off. Every problem was studied and results were made available to the designers of the Gemini and Apollo spacecraft, whose contracts had been let at the same time. Project Mercury was at a crossroads. Flight confidence had been developed and the question now was whether or not to begin to pursue the goals that were immediately beyond the original Mercury objectives. For every question that the first four Mercury flights had answered, many more were generated by each event in every flight.

The space program was beginning to pyramid. As NASA prepared for a lunar landing, public interest in Mercury increased.

The first real Mercury textbook flight was Sigma 7, flown by Walter Schirra on October 3, 1962. Schirra flew 9 hours and 13 minutes. His flight was needed tonic for the American spirit. Earlier that summer the Soviets had launched Vostok III, a five-ton craft that carried Major Andrian G. Nikolayev as cosmonaut. American space officials thought that the flight was a re-run of Titov's until Radio Moscow announced that Pavel R. Popovich had been launched in Vostok IV and had sighted Nikolayev. Officials feared that the Soviets planned to rendezvous in space, but the Falcon and Golden Eagle (Vostoks III and IV) did not meet in space. It became apparent that while the Soviets had the technical ability to launch back-to-back flights, the maneuverability of their craft was inferior to the much smaller Mercury.

With the Soviets moving ahead in the space race, President Kennedy was under intense pressure to defend his commitment to a lunar landing. He answered his critics in a speech at Rice University in Houston, Texas:

> We set sail on this new sea because there is knowledge to be gained and rights to be won, and they must be won and used for the progress of all people. For space science, like nuclear science and all technology, has no conscience of its own. Whether it will become a form of good or ill depends on us, and only if the United States occupies a position of preeminence can we help decide whether this new ocean will be a sea of peace or a new, terrifying theater of war. . . . Space can be explored and mastered without feeding the fires of war, without repeating the mistake that man has made in extending his writ around this globe of ours.

Critics continued to attack the space program. Senator William Fulbright of Arkansas called it wasteful, but President Kennedy's commitment had been taken seriously at NASA, and of the 2,500 employees at the Manned Spacecraft Center, only 500 were working on Mercury. The rest were involved with the future Gemini and Apollo programs.

The final Mercury flight was Gordon Cooper's in Faith 7. This flight, described by Cooper himself as "one big camera," was the most scientifically oriented Mercury mission.

With the data collected by Faith 7, NASA had the information that it needed from Mercury. Proposals had been made for a three-day Mercury flight, but many felt that continuing Mercury at the risk of losing the funding for other programs would be foolish when the necessary information for later programs had already been obtained. It would be twenty-two months before Americans would fly in space again, and NASA was worried that the public would lose interest in the space program during the time that Project Gemini and its two-man, maneuverable ship was being made ready.

Project Mercury had lasted fifty-five months and had cost $384,131,000—less than the total cost of the New York World's Fair of 1964. While the project was being carried to its successful conclusion, the Soviets launched three more spacecraft, Vostoks V and VI in 1963 and a three-man Voshkod in 1964. Vostok VI carried Valentina Tereshkova, the first and only female to fly in space. Not a trained space pilot, Tereshkova flew as a passenger in a ground-controlled spacecraft.

GEMINI

Flown by a new crew of astronauts, the Gemini craft would be the first real spaceship. It would be the only craft that could maneuver in space, change orbits, and meet with other spacecraft in space.

The Gemini spacecraft was different from the previous Mercury craft. Aircraft ejection seats were substituted for an escape tower, and a modular unit was added so that repairs and alterations could be made as the mission required. Gemini would be the last American manned craft to use a military booster. In addition, it would give future moon missions the necessary practice with sophisticated space hardware to complete a successful moon mission.

Employing the same bell-shape as Mercury, the Gemini craft had more than twice Mercury's volume. It carried a computer of amazing sophistication as well as crew comforts that, while limited, had been unheard of on Mercury.

The long delay between Mercury and Gemini, the successful launching of three Russians in orbit, and the assassination of President Kennedy dampened enthusiasm for the first Gemini checkout flight scheduled for March, 1965. President Kennedy's death had a profound effect on NASA. Although President Johnson thoroughly favored a strong space program, the space effort would miss the eloquent support of the slain President. When President Johnson asked Mrs. Kennedy what memorial would be most suited to her husband's ideals, Mrs. Kennedy suggested that the memorial have something to do with the national space program. Thus, in 1964 Cape Canaveral became Cape Kennedy.*

On March 23, 1965, the first manned Gemini flight was launched. The Titan II booster lifted off into the first orbit of a modest three-orbit checkout flight. Spacecraft commander Virgil Grissom tested the new machine and found it satisfactory. The orbit was altered, the onboard computer was used, and for the first time in history a spacecraft maneuvered in space.

The Gemini program faced a more complicated test during the flight of Gemini IV. If the American moon landing program depended on any one technique, it was the technique of rendezvous and docking, first tested on this flight. Midcourse corrections, radar, and ground support were tested on both Gemini IV and Gemini V.

* Residents of the Cape have several times attempted to have the name changed back to Canaveral, but their efforts have met with only limited popular support. To avoid confusion, Cape Canaveral will be referred to as Cape Kennedy throughout the rest of this volume.

The rendezvous target vehicle for Gemini IV was to be an Atlas-Agena. It took off on time on October 25, 1965, but because of an upper stage failure did not achieve orbit. Instead of playing havoc with mission schedules, the Agena failure led to the most spectacular space flight in world history. Gemini IV and her Titan booster were removed from the launch pad and placed in storage. The Gemini VII booster was quickly checked out and erected for a fourteen-day endurance flight.

On December 4, 1965, Gemini VII was launched. Gemini VI, whose mission was to rendezvous with Gemini VII, was erected on the pad and prepared for launching on December 12. The countdown reached zero. Smoke and flame appeared. Suddenly, a shutdown. The flight engineers could not understand why this manned vehicle had failed on the pad. High atop the booster, Walter Schirra, commander of the spacecraft, saw no apparent damage to the booster and did not eject himself and his copilot from the craft. This was a crucial decision. Schirra's judgment was vindicated when it was discovered that a plastic plug left in the booster had caused the near tragic shutdown. Three days later Schirra and his crewmate flew into orbit and moved to within a foot of Gemini VII. The world was amazed at the ease with which the two craft found each other.

The Gemini VI flight was the turning point in the space competition with the Soviets. Gemini's sophistication now seemed more advanced than the larger Soviet spacecraft, and the Saturn booster was by this time well under development without one flight failure to its already impressive record. The long-range Gemini program requirements had been met. Now all that remained was the docking procedure that would be undertaken by Gemini VIII.

Neil Armstrong and David Scott achieved a perfect docking with their Gemini VIII spaceship, but they became the first Americans in danger of dying in space. Shortly after

docking, an attitude-control thruster was stuck in an on position and the combination Gemini-Agena began to spin uncon-
trollably. For the first time the back-up contingencies of the
spacecraft were called upon in a life-or-death situation. Re-
entry rockets were fired to control and stabilize the craft
seconds before the point of blackout. The astronauts re-
entered the atmosphere in the western Pacific, and a recovery
aircraft watched the capsule drop gently into the ocean.

Gemini IX conducted more sophisticated rendezvous techniques, and it maneuvered itself into an orbit 476 miles high.
Docking was impossible because the troublesome Agena
failed to eject its protective launch shroud. It looked to the
astronauts as though they were facing an angry alligator.
Gemini XI and XII completed the rendezvous and docking
techniques originally called for in the program.

Perhaps the most harrowing and exciting achievements of
this period of space exploration were the experiments with
extravehicular activities (EVA). A short EVA was first
achieved by the Soviets in the spring of 1965. On Gemini IV
pilot Edward White worked outside of his craft in his space-
suit for 23 minutes. While the Soviet flight program slowed
down, the U.S. began to do more extravehicular work. On
Gemini IX, Eugene Cernan worked for two hours outside
his craft. The most spectacular EVA in Project Gemini was
conducted by Michael Collins, who visited a docked Agena to
recover an experiment.

An impressive total of 111 scientific experiments were carried out in the Gemini program; 90 of these produced useful
results. About 1,500 color photographs of the earth were
taken. One Gemini XII photo was to have enormous value
in support of the geological theory of continental drift.

Gemini proved that man could work and live in space for
long enough periods to justify an attempt at a lunar landing.
Gemini also proved a variety of NASA management ideas.
For the first time a program was completed ahead of deadline.

Gemini XII flew in November, 1966, rather than in early
1967 as originally planned three years before. Project Gemini
cost the country $1.29 billion and flew men in space on ten
missions for several thousand hours.

By the end of Gemini, NASA was functioning at full force.
Construction of its massive moon launch complex was well
under way. The Manned Spacecraft Center at Houston was in
full charge, ready for the earth-orbit test mission of Project
Apollo only four months after the completion of the Gemini
project.

VI

Americans on the Moon

It is history now. President Kennedy had proposed it, Congress had accepted it, and NASA had executed the goal of landing a man on the moon before the 1960's had run their turbulent course. Project Apollo, as the moon project was called, cost a little over $20 billion dollars, almost exactly what NASA had predicted it would cost in 1961. The project involved some half a million workers directly and millions of others indirectly.

In 1962, Congress responded to President Kennedy's request and granted NASA a budget of $1.6 billion. NASA was clearly aware of the enormous effort that lay ahead of it, as illustrated by a letter that Deputy Administrator Hugh L. Dryden wrote to Senator Robert S. Kerr on June 22, 1961. The attainment of the goal, he wrote,

> requires extensive research and development in almost every branch of science and technology at the frontiers of knowledge in these various fields. New materials and components must be developed to function in the extreme cold and the extremely low pressures of outer space, at the extreme speeds, and at the extreme temperatures attained in rocket combustion chambers and on the outer surface of bodies re-entering the atmosphere at

high speed. New developments in propulsion, in electronics, in communications, in guidance and control techniques, in computer techniques, are necessary in order to accomplish the task. New information in the life sciences, including the effects of the radiations encountered in outer space, the effects of long periods of weightlessness, and long exposure to a completely closed environment—all these are required and will provide new basic information about the performance of the human body under adverse conditions. This new knowledge and experience in the space sciences and technologies will provide the sound basis for applying our newfound knowledge to the design of space vehicles for a variety of purposes, some now foreseen, others unthought of at present. These applications include not only space vehicles for scientific research, for communications systems, for meteorological observation, and presently unforeseen civil uses, but also space vehicles for potential applications in the national defense. Space technology, like aeronautical technology, can be applied to military systems, and we must be well advanced in this technology to avoid its possible exploitation against us.

Behind this statement of intent, momentous as it was in terms of public policy, lay a number of motivating incidents. On March 22, 1961, President Kennedy had called a White House meeting to determine what action should be taken on a supplemental appropriation for NASA's budget for fiscal year 1962. Of concern to the President and his advisers were the needs to increase the rate of closure on the Soviet Union's lead in weightlifting capacity in space and to advance manned exploration of space beyond Project Mercury. The outcome of this meeting was the recognition that large booster development held the key to space mastery, and a clear decision was made for the United States to accelerate its space effort in an attempt to attain leadership in the race with the U.S.S.R.

The next step was taken on April 20, 1961, when President Kennedy asked Vice-President Lyndon Johnson, as Chairman of the National Aeronautics and Space Council, to make an over-all survey of the U.S. position in the space effort.

Beginning on April 22, 1961, Johnson chaired several meetings variously attended by members of the Congress, NASA, the general public, the Department of Defense, the Bureau of the Budget, the President's Science Adviser, and the Executive Secretary of the National Aeronautics and Space Council. Although no formal record was kept of these meetings, it was reported that the Vice-President would answer any doubts or hesitancy concerning costs with the question, "Well, would you rather be a second-rate nation and not spend quite so much money?"

The meetings concluded on April 28, and the results were summarized in a five-and-one-half-page report in which the Vice-President advised that the lunar landing project offered a real opportunity for the U.S. to take the lead in space exploration, possibly by 1966 or 1967.

In a show of unity usually reserved for declarations of war, Congress overwhelmingly supported the initial funding requests. The lunar landing assumed the dimensions of a national imperative, and a vast mobilization of men, money, and materials was soon under way. Within a matter of months the goal became a test not only of America's skills but of its perseverance.

Although some commentators have voiced the opinion that the lunar landing decision was made by the White House to offset the Bay of Pigs fiasco, the record shows that the planning was long in the making, and the decision would have been the same in any event. A few voices were raised then, as later, to say that the moon landing program was symptomatic of America's mistaken priorities, and that it made no sense to spend $20 billion to put a man on the moon while denying funds to programs that would put millions of disadvantaged Americans back on their feet on the American earth.

Against the background of the cold war, the decision to land on the moon was considered by Vice-President Johnson to be justified. He said:

To reach the moon is a risk, but it is a risk we must take. Failure to go into space is even riskier. . . . One can predict with confidence that failure to master space means being second best in every aspect, in the crucial area of our cold war world. In the eyes of the world first in space is first, period; second in space is second in everything.

It took little more than half a century to get from the Wright brothers' crude flying machine to the jumbo jet. With Project Apollo, NASA was faced with covering a far greater technological distance—from the relatively crude American rocketry of World War II to a manned lunar landing in less than half that time.

THE MANAGEMENT STRUGGLE

Within NASA, one of the most difficult problems from the organizational standpoint was assigning the manned space flight program a position in the headquarters structure that would match the amount of money allotted to it. One suggestion was to establish a semiautonomous bureau within NASA, completely self-sufficient in terms of staff. The opposite school of thought considered the bureau approach undesirable and thought the locus of power should be in NASA's general management. The imbalance between the manned lunar landing program and the rest of NASA was a source of much management turmoil.

Recognizing the need to establish manned space flight activities as an entity, NASA established a management council in December, 1961, chaired by the new manned space flight program director, D. Brainerd Holmes. Other members of the council were Wernher von Braun, Director of the George C. Marshall Space Flight Center, Robert R. Gilruth, Director of the Manned Spacecraft Center, and the principal assistants to the three senior officials. In March, 1962, when the NASA installation at Cape Kennedy was established as a separate field center, its director, Kurt H. Debus, and his deputy also became members of the management council.

As national and international interest in the astronauts heightened, officials of the manned space flight program were encouraged to intensify their arguments for even higher funding priority within the NASA program, and Holmes, as director of the program, proposed a supplemental appropriation of $400 million for fiscal year 1963 to speed the manned lunar landing effort. Von Braun and Gilruth also supported this request.

NASA Administrator James Webb felt differently. In his view, the leaders of Congress had high respect for an agency that could execute programs in an orderly fashion by funding for a year at a time and avoiding such emergency actions as supplemental budget requests, which further complicate an already complex budgetary process. In addition, he wanted to emphasize the necessity for Congress to assume its full responsibility to act on the regular budget. Accordingly, the Administrator decided to seek any needed increased funding in the regular budget for the following year. Officials of the manned space flight organization did not accept this reasoning. They wanted to request the funds while the climate was favorable.

After failing to gain support for a supplemental appropriation, Holmes suggested that funds might be reprogrammed into the manned space flight program from other NASA programs. Webb was even more opposed to this suggestion. He believed that any serious redirection of funds appropriated for other programs would seriously reduce the effectiveness of the science, technology, and applications areas and the NASA field centers and would weaken the agency's basic capability.

Within the next two weeks, reports of the disagreement

had found their way to the public press, and on November 21 reached the White House. Vice-President Johnson and senior NASA officials, including D. Brainerd Holmes, met with President Kennedy to review NASA's budget and the question of a supplemental appropriation for the coming year. Associate Administrator Robert C. Seamans recalled later that President Kennedy considered the manned lunar landing the most important U.S. objective in space exploration, while Webb argued that the main objective was for the country to become pre-eminent in space. He would not take responsibility for a program that was not properly balanced. The President suggested that Webb put his ideas in writing "so that I can really see whether we're working together or not." Webb complied. In a nine-page letter he declared:

> The manned lunar landing program, although of highest national priority, will not by itself create the pre-eminent position we seek. The present interest of the United States in terms of our scientific posture and increasing prestige, and our future interest in terms of having an adequate scientific and technological base for space activities beyond the manned lunar landing, demand that we pursue an adequate, well-balanced space program in all areas, including those not directly related to the manned lunar landing. We strongly believe that the United States will gain tangible benefits from such a total accumulation of basic scientific and technological data as well as from the greatly increased strength of our educational institutions. For these reasons, we believe it would not be in the nation's long-range interest to cancel or drastically curtail on-going space science and technology development programs in order to increase the funding of the manned lunar landing program in fiscal year 1963.

In the end, President Kennedy decided not to request a supplemental appropriation. Webb had preserved his management prerogatives on a major policy issue. Holmes announced his resignation the following June.

From the viewpoint of management, the most important effect of the Webb-Holmes clash was the reorganization that resulted after Dr. George E. Mueller was named Deputy Associate Administrator of NASA for Manned Space Flight on September 3, 1963. The result of Mueller's changes combined with the comprehensive agency reorganization of November, 1962, was that some 14,000 employees at NASA headquarters and the three manned space flight centers became responsible for managing the efforts of approximately 200,000 people in the contractor structure of the Apollo program. In addition to shifting the power of decision back to the centers, while leaving the task of providing over-all policy guidance and review to headquarters, a NASA-industry group was formed in October, 1964, composed of top executives of all major Apollo program contractors, the Associate Administrator for Manned Space Flight, and directors of the three NASA field centers.

THE FLIGHT PROGRAM

The Apollo program called for the flights of twelve Saturn 1B and fifteen Saturn V launch vehicles with associated spacecraft systems before the end of the decade. NASA management also decided to adopt the "all-up" flight testing pattern for the Apollo Saturn space vehicles, which meant that each launch vehicle flight would use live stages and essentially complete spacecraft.

This testing plan had several advantages. First, a large amount of data on all space vehicle systems could be acquired in each flight, providing early information needed for final design. Second, much could be learned from successful test flights. In a step-by-step flight program, where several flights of each component were scheduled before the next was added, a completely successful flight could often not be followed by a rapid step to the next, more complex, combination because the flight hardware would not yet be available. In the all-up concept, the components would be ready to move on to the next phase of the test program. This technique put heavy emphasis on exhaustive ground testing of one component at a time, in sequence, then in combination, until complete flight systems were ground tested as a unit.

A third important advantage of this new approach was that it shortened the schedule and reduced the projected cost of the total program. This was made necessary by the budget reduction of $612 million for fiscal year 1964, unless the rest of the NASA space program was to be virtually eliminated. The consequence of the budget adjustment was a somewhat higher risk of failure on any specific flight, due to the inclusion of more unknowns, and the resultant reduction of some of the margin for error built into the program at the time of initial planning.

Under the all-up test concept, the first Saturn 1B launch would take place in 1966 and the first manned Saturn 1B would be launched in 1967. The first Saturn V launch was scheduled for later in 1967, and the first manned Saturn V flight for 1968, leading to the first manned lunar landing before the end of the decade. The total cost estimate for this revised program, including Apollo research and development, construction of facilities, tracking and data acquisition, and operation costs, was established in March, 1964, at $19.5 billion.

Alterations made necessary in the total program had narrowed the scope of the Apollo effort, focusing it more exclusively on achieving the manned lunar landing goal. With better-defined requirements and detailed design knowledge, and under the pressure of budget reductions, assurance of reaching the goal had been increased, but most of the margin, the hedge against unforeseen problems, had been removed.

A Tragedy and Its Aftermath

The highly successful U.S. manned program received its first massive blow not in the abyss of space but 210 feet above Pad 34 at Cape Kennedy during dinner hour on January 27, 1967. The routine radio messages transmitted during ground test 204 of the first manned Apollo capsule became suddenly strange and horrifying. Technical readouts were replaced by the shrieks of three astronauts being burned to death. The men were trying to escape from the capsule but found themselves trapped. The hatch, designed to provide maximum safety during translunar flight and high-speed re-entry into the atmosphere, opened inward, and it was impossible for the astronauts to open it against the high pressures created by the fire inside the spacecraft.

A review board named for the 204 fire, as it was called, found that the fire had started within the sealed spacecraft and had spread rapidly through the 100 per cent oxygen atmosphere, burning through the space suits, destroying the breathing atmosphere of the astronauts, and then, as the pressure increased, rupturing the Apollo capsule.

Safety considerations in design had always emphasized eliminating possible ignition sources in an oxygen atmosphere and limiting the combustible material inside the spacecraft, but since the routine ground test was taking place aboard an unfueled booster, it was considered technically nonhazardous, so material not approved for flight was allowed to be present in the spacecraft. This consisted of a nylon net to catch objects inadvertently dropped during the test, and a foam cushion on which to rest the inner hatch during crew exit practice. These materials, highly combustible in the pressurized oxygen atmosphere, conveyed the fire rapidly across the spacecraft when the shell was ruptured by rising pressure.

Although NASA officials were able to report to a Senate hearing within a month that corrective actions were already under way to remedy the deficiencies in the program that may have contributed to the tragedy, it was evident that, before the Apollo program had a reasonable chance of moving forward safely, the amount of redesign, retest, and requalification that had to be done would set the program back at least eighteen months. Furthermore, the fire had had a major impact on the morale and confidence of the entire NASA organization, as well as on the relationships between the government manager and industrial contractor, and between Congress and NASA.

The final report of the Apollo 204 Review Board showed that the Apollo spacecraft was a "death trap under the conditions of the test, and the astronauts could not have escaped the fire once it started." The conditions responsible for the disaster were enumerated:

A sealed cabin, pressurized with an oxygen aymosphere
Extensive distribution of combustible materials in the cabin
Vulnerable wiring carrying spacecraft power
Vulnerable plumbing carrying a combustible and corrosive coolant
Inadequate provisions for the crew to escape
Inadequate provisions for rescue or medical assistance

The Apollo team, the board said, failed to give adequate attention to mundane but vital questions of crew safety, and deficiencies were found in the design, engineering, and quality control of manufacture of the spacecraft.

The ensuing congressional investigation studied the mishap even further. The investigators were especially aroused by the fact that NASA would not make available a report by the Apollo program director at NASA Headquarters, Major General Samuel C. Phillips, which advised NASA management that the Apollo contractor, North American, was badly behind schedule and that the lunar landing schedule was in jeopardy. Phillips had sent a letter to North American on December 19, 1965, in which he expressed his dissatisfaction regarding hardware performance, increasing costs, welding difficulties, insulation bonding, and redesign as a result of component failures during qualification. He was especially critical of North American's "passive" management attitude. The main area of corporate interests, Phillips reported, "appears to be in the financial outlook and in the cost estimating and proposal effort."

In refusing to release the Phillips report as Congress requested, Administrator Webb argued that its disclosure would kill the goose that laid the golden egg. Members of Congress demanded to know what NASA had done to remedy the conditions at North American in the thirteen months between the Phillips report and the fire. When it appeared that nothing had been done, the Senate Space Committee concluded that NASA's "overconfidence" and "complacency" had contributed to the disaster. As a result, management personnel changes ensued both at North American and at NASA. Public concern was allayed, and the manned space flight program forged ahead on a revised schedule. The tragic fire seemed to have ended America's chances of putting the first man on the moon, although Associate Administrator Seamans believed that there was still a slim chance that the Kennedy goal could be met.

Cost Increases

Cost increases for the Apollo program in fiscal year 1967 amounted to nearly half a billion dollars over the previous year's estimate. To understand the cost requirements which necessitate such increases, some idea of the costs involved in spacecraft design, research, development, and production is necessary. A basic introduction may be gained from the fact that the lunar module which landed the first two astronauts on the moon cost fifteen times its weight in gold ($20 million per ton of weight as against $1.3 million per ton for gold at a free market rate of $42 an ounce). This is not to imply that the lunar module or the Apollo system itself was gold-plated, but it does help to illustrate the staggering engineering complexities involved. The Saturn V-Apollo combination has more than 8 million parts, which have to be checked by computers before launch, and which need, in addition, 100 engineers to monitor each step. From assembly to launch, 10 miles of tape are consumed to store the 2.5 million bits of data that ensure launch readiness. If there were no automatic equipment, it would take 500 men to check each subsystem and correlate their findings—an impossible, endless task that would see swarms of technicians colliding with each other as they tried to get firsthand data in real time, to say nothing of the logging and correlating chores that would be so time-consuming as to be self-defeating. As it is, the ground computer system constantly pulses 2,700 discrete checkout points and computes a total picture of the over-all status of the vehicle at 150,000 signals a minute, all with a view to discovering potential weaknesses and preventing failure before any commitment to press the firing button has been made.

Major costs also involved building the infrastructure for manned space flight. Support facilities worth $2.2 billion were located at the Kennedy Space Center, the Manned Spacecraft Center near Houston, the Marshall Space Flight Center, and elsewhere. In addition, there was a worldwide tracking, communication, and command and control network built and operated to meet the needs of manned space flight. As originally created for the Mercury program, this network consisted of eighteen earth stations around the globe, including two ships. So efficient had been the performance of this network during the Mercury program that the Gemini program had been able to run with only twelve stations—ten on land and two at sea.

For the Apollo project, the transmission of huge volumes of data—television, voice, and electronic commands at lunar distances—required new stations that were co-located with Deep Space Network Stations at Goldstone, California, Madrid, Spain, and Canberra, Australia. These stations were equipped with 85-foot dish antennas and highly automated data handling and processing equipment, along with specially designed receiving, transmitting, and ranging systems, all using one antenna, in what has come to be known as the unified S-band system.

For Apollo, three additional instrumentation ships were added where land stations were not feasible, bringing the total number of ships to five, while the number of land stations was increased to fifteen. In addition, eight instrumented jet aircraft were contracted for. Since studies showed that land and sea linkages alone would not give Mission Control Center at Houston the real-time linkages it needed, communications satellites were also provided for. It was NASA's multimillion-dollar contract with the Communications Satellite Corporation that formed the hard core upon which the international system was founded (Chapter X). Spurred on by NASA's needs for Apollo, the corporation accelerated its planning and put international commercial communications satellites into service nearly two years ahead of the originally planned dates. All told, the communications core of the manned space flight program represented an investment of $300 million in facilities. Coupled with operating costs, the total was $1.2 billion, 5 per cent of NASA's $24 billion total costs to date for manned space flight.

Apollo 7

Veteran astronaut Walter Schirra and his crew, Donn Eisele and R. Walter Cunningham, flew the first manned Apollo mission after the 204 fire. It was the first U.S. three-man mission, and the first manned mission to be launched by other than a military rocket. Schirra, to NASA's consternation, stated publicly that he would not fly the mission until he and his crew were convinced that their craft was spaceworthy, and he spent long days going over every detail of the most advanced and complicated spaceship that NASA had produced up to that time. By Mercury and Gemini standards, it was huge. It featured numerous crew comforts, more spacious quarters, and hot meals. Capable of performing extended missions in deep space, it was designed so that it could be used later in conjunction with the first space station, Skylab.

Apollo 7 was launched on October 11, 1968. For the first time, live telecasts were transmitted to earth from a U.S. spacecraft. There were seven of these, but Schirra was more concerned with the mission than with entertaining the public. The Apollo craft performed beautifully, and the service propulsion engine fired perfectly. Head colds impaired the dispositions of the crew, but the problems expected with three free-floating crew members simply did not materialize.

The Apollo 7 flight lasted for more than 260 hours and paved the way for a NASA decision few Americans ever expected.

Circumlunar Flight

On November 12, 1968, NASA Administrator Thomas Paine made this announcement: "After careful and thorough examination of all the systems and risks involved, we have concluded that we are now ready to fly the most advanced mission for our Apollo 8 launch in December, the orbit around the moon."

At 7:51 A.M. on December 21, 1968, astronauts Frank Borman, James Lovell, and William Anders left the earth aboard Apollo 8. Such a flight had been far from the minds of space flight scientists on the night of the tragic fire almost two years before. On Christmas Eve, Apollo 8 went into orbit around the moon. A view of the moon's surface, sixty-one miles below, was transmitted back to earth via television, and for the first time since the 204 accident NASA officials began to speak of a lunar landing during the coming year.

By then it had become clear that the Soviet program was in deep trouble. A giant booster, bigger than the Saturn V, had exploded on its launch pad, and in April, 1967, a lone cosmonaut, traveling in the new Soviet Soyuz, had been killed when the capsule's landing system failed. Subsequent Soviet flights led one to believe that the Soviet Union had abandoned the lunar race and had decided to explore the planets and the moon with robot spacecraft, using their manned capability exclusively for the construction of space stations.

In October, 1968, a Russian cosmonaut carried out a four-day reflight of the first, tragic Soyuz flight, and on January 14, 1969, another cosmonaut flew in Soyuz IV. The next day he was joined by three cosmonauts in Soyuz V. The two vehicles rendezvoused and performed a docking exercise like that the United States had done in 1965. One of the cosmonauts then returned to earth in a vehicle other than that in which he had left, which proved that earth-orbit rescue is more than a slight possibility, providing back-up hardware is available.

Less than two months later, on March 3, 1969, NASA launched its first "all-up" Apollo on a Saturn V into earth orbit. On this mission the lunar module was tested, and docking was accomplished with the moon landing equipment. The long-duration flight lasted 241 hours. Many believed that NASA would change its mind and land Apollo 10 on the moon, but, with the lunar landing in sight, NASA wanted one more test flight.

Apollo 10 was destined to be a dress rehearsal for the first real moon landing. On May 18, Apollo 10 lifted off and several days later entered lunar orbit. As if preparing for the actual landing, astronauts Thomas Stafford, John Young, and Eugene Cernan readied the landing module for separation. Two of the astronauts entered it and descended to within nine miles of the lunar surface. All went well until the landing craft fired its ascent stage to rejoin the command module. The firing was much rougher than expected and caused one of the astronauts to scream out "Son of a bitch!" Aside from this, the mission ended with as much grace as it had begun.

THE MOON LANDINGS

John Kennedy's goal, which had seemed almost impossible of achievement eight years before, was attained on July 20, 1969, at 4:17 P.M. Eastern standard time, when the spacecraft Eagle landed at Tranquility Base on the moon. The moon race was over. Up until the end, the Soviet Union attempted to land a robot craft on the moon to scoop up a soil sample and return to earth before the crew of Apollo 11 could land, but it was not in the cards. The Soviet craft had crashed.

Six hours and thirty-nine minutes after the spacecraft had landed, astronaut Neil Armstrong stepped onto the lunar surface with the remark, "That's one small step for a man, one giant leap for mankind." In the United States alone, over 29 million households watched the lunar landing on television, and an additional 10 million saw at least part of the moon walk. Overnight the names Neil Armstrong, Michael Collins, and Edwin Aldrin became familiar to most of the . world. In Japan, it was estimated that 70 million people watched the landing and the moon walk. The story was the same all over the world with the total global television audience estimated by the U.S. Information Agency at 650 million persons. The landing was greeted with cheers for American technology. There were calls for an end to conflict among nations, and sighs of relief that the adventure had proceeded without mishap. For days, newspapers and radio throughout the world described the historic space journey in dozens of languages.

For an all too brief spell, mankind was united by a common experience that deeply affected the way that people felt about themselves as human beings. The euphoria was short-lived, but for the moment man's reach seemed to be infinite, and few problems seemed truly insurmountable.

Through the first lunar landing in 1969, which marked the attainment of President Kennedy's goal, the Apollo project had cost a little over $21.3 billion. This figure, however, included a surplus of $2 billion in hardware, bringing the actual lunar landing cost down to $19.3 billion.

A second voyage was launched on November 14, 1969, landing astronauts Charles Conrad and Alan Bean on the moon's Ocean of Storms and bringing them safely back to earth on November 24. But, like any other repeated experience, the novelty of lunar flight wore thin. Although the scientific import of the second flight was greater than that of the first, the public impact was less. It seemed as if the voyages were so perfect that they lacked drama and suspense. Any complacency that may have existed, however, was rudely shattered by the nearly catastrophic flight of Apollo 13. After a perfect lift-off on April 11, 1970, the astronauts' main oxygen supply was lost when an oxygen tank exploded on the way to the moon. The review board established by NASA to inquire into the causes of the failure was forthright in its criticism. It found that the spacecraft lost its main oxygen supply because of "an unusual combination of mistakes by men on the ground." It cited contractors for installing wrong thermostats, for subjecting the tanks to rough handling and cited NASA's own employees for failing to monitor the tank properly when it underwent preflight tests on the launch pad.

"The potential was there for a major conflagration on the launch pad," Review Board Chairman Edgar Cortright, Director of the Langley Research Center, conceded at a press conference. "If the oxygen tank had burst on the pad, the propellants in the service module could have been ignited and the entire launch vehicle destroyed." Cortright also admitted that the lessons of the Apollo 204 fire had not been fully applied. After the Apollo fire, NASA management had put a major effort into redesigning the command module and the lunar module but a lesser effort into the service module, where the Apollo 13 accident occurred.

Because of its unsparing, tell-it-like-it-is quality, the review board report was accepted by many as an indication of NASA's maturity in that it was willing to probe relentlessly for weaknesses in its own operations. However, the explosion that rocked Apollo 13 did more than challenge comfortable assumptions about manned space flight. It reminded the country of how much had been taken for granted, how much had been achieved, and how far man had yet to go. When the emergency came, the illusion of perfectability was shattered. There was nothing easy or certain about space flight after all. While the event did not signal the end of manned space flight, it caused a closer and more critical look to be taken at the program as a whole, including its costs and scientific returns.

In the sober stock-taking that followed the accident, there seemed to be general recognition that some of NASA's more sanguine dreams were not so easily attainable. Manned flight to Mars, for example, seemed further away than ever, and there was consensus that the more immediate concerns of the space program would be directed to missions that provided data related to the earth's own environment and resources.

The reworking of the Apollo service module caused Apollo 14 to be postponed until January, 1971, and two lunar landings in the series of six more that had been planned were canceled because of budget constraints. Not only was the cancellation protested by the nation's thirty-nine top lunar scientists, who saw one-third of the planned lunar surface experiments eliminated, but others saw the manned space flight program running downhill nearly as fast as it had run up. There was even some feeling that the entire manned space flight program might turn out to have been the most spectacular and expensive stunt in history rather than the first step in a genuine effort to learn more about some of the secrets of the universe.

Led by Administrator Paine, NASA's management made no secret of the hard choices confronting the agency in a time of budgetary and fiscal stringency in 1970. They were quick to admit that their principal concern was to preserve adequate resources for the post-Apollo space program, which involved a manned Skylab orbital workshop to be launched in November, 1972, and visited by three-man crews for twenty-eight days and, later, for fifty-six days. After the third Skylab mission, planned for 1973, manned space flight would probably grind to a halt for three to five years while waiting for the development of the first space shuttle. Furthermore, NASA's manned exploration of the moon would possibly not be resumed until the 1980's, when a nuclear space engine would be ready for operation.

Having achieved the lunar landing within the promised decade, NASA's management was faced with the problem of maintaining an appropriate balance by utilizing existing capabilities to make further gains in science, applications, and technology, while at the same time advancing the state-of-the-art so that in decades to come still greater rewards could be obtained.

With Apollo 14, NASA reached a new level of maturity. Alan Shepard, who had orbited the earth ten years before, was forty-seven at the time he made the third moon landing in January, 1971—two years older than President Kennedy had been when he made the decision to send men to the moon. Shepard's 1961 Redstone/Mercury rocket had less thrust than the escape rocket on his 1971 Saturn/Apollo. The

Apollo 14 spacecraft alone weighed 100,000 pounds, out-
weighing Shepard's combined Redstone booster and Mercury
craft by 15 tons. Between Shepard's first and second flights,
Americans had spent 7,000 hours in space and had flown 32
million miles.

Apollo 14 was the last of the "engineering" Apollo flights.
It came at a time of severe cutbacks. From the perspective of
Washington, space flight is political; to Kennedy Space Center personnel it is intensely personal, and the Center staged a
morale-boosting campaign for the flight for fear that careless-
ness might result in disaster. But Apollo 14 was successful,
and it was beautiful to watch. The next moon flight, Apollo
15, with its Lunar Roving Vehicle and its ambitious scientific
program, was something more and did much to allay public
apathy and cynicism toward the space program.

On the night of July 25, 1971, just hours before Apollo 15
was launched, a heat-lightning storm struck Cape Kennedy,
brilliantly illuminating the Saturn V rocket, which was visible
across the flatlands of Florida for fifty miles. The rocket's
service tower was 500 feet high and weighed 10.5 million
pounds. The Vehicle Assembly Building, three miles west of
the tower, was fifty-three stories high. Its 456-foot doors could
easily accommodate the United Nations Building in New
York. The Saturn rocket, weighing 6 million pounds, had
been moved from the assembly building to its launch pad by
a "crawler" weighing 6,000 tons (its "mileage" was 22 feet
per gallon of fuel). The mobile launcher and rocket together
weighed 20 million pounds. Nothing heavier has ever been
moved over land.

If something goes wrong with a Saturn rocket and it ex-
plodes, the explosion can be as lethal as that of an atomic
bomb, so no one not on the crew was allowed closer to the
rocket than 3.5 miles. On the morning of July 26, 1971, 8.9
seconds before launch time, the watchers at the distant press
site saw fire pour from the base of the launch pad as the en-

gines began to build thrust. Giant hold-down clamps restrained the Saturn rocket until she had power. A few seconds later the pad came alight, the long access arms to the booster pulled away, and sheets of ice were seen to break loose from the struggling rocket.

The astronauts in their Apollo spacecraft, covered with a launch shroud, saw nothing. At time zero, the clamps were released and Saturn was liberated. She was already climbing when the sound waves reached the press site and rippled the clothing of the newsmen. At two thousand feet, the flame of the Saturn still touched the earth. Steam and heat waves from her engines blanketed the horizon. In the clear sky, the Saturn arched over like a thirty-six-story building flying through space. The 140-foot first stage dropped away, and Apollo 15 left for the moon.

The mission had been prefaced by another tragedy in the Soviet space program. On June 30, 1971, after breaking the American endurance record in space aboard the mini-space station Salute, three cosmonauts boarded their Soyuz for re-entry. Apparently the hatch was not properly closed, and upon separation of the re-entry cabin of the Soyuz, the cosmonauts died. The Soviet press announced the deaths candidly, and doubts were expressed about the safety of the Apollo 15 astronauts by those not familiar with the Apollo atmospheric system, which is under much lower pressure than the Soviet system.

These fears proved groundless. Apollo 15 was the most successful scientific space expedition up to that time. Broadcasts from the color television camera temporarily renewed public interest in the program. The Lunar Roving Vehicle performed beautifully, and for the first time the astronauts appeared to have a working confidence in their role on the moon.

Two more moon landings were made before the Apollo program was complete. So many minor things went wrong in the early stages of Apollo 16 in April, 1972, that the lunar landing was almost scrubbed. After the landing was made, the mission proceeded perfectly, but public interest was at an all-time low. Despite the scientific success of the mission, the public just did not seem interested. Interest was revived later in the year by Apollo 17, which promised to be the last manned flight to outer space for years to come.

On the night of December 6, 1972, 3,000 correspondents from all over the world assembled at Cape Kennedy to witness the first night lift-off in the Apollo program. Another first was occasioned by a "hold" in the final few seconds of the countdown, but the problem was mastered, and in the small hours of December 7 Apollo 17 left for the moon, trailing a spectacular tail of flame, 3,000 feet long and 500 feet in diameter, that literally turned night into day above the Florida coast. Again, there was a perfect landing on the moon and an abundance of clear television pictures. More rock and soil samples were brought back than had been collected on any other mission, and the multibillion-dollar Apollo program was terminated with a faultless splashdown in the Pacific.

VII

NASA and Congress

NASA is a child of Congress rather than of the executive branch. In the fall of 1957, Congress responded to the news of the first Russian Sputnik not in wonderment but in anger. Congress was angry at President Dwight D. Eisenhower and his staff for treating space as if it were not scientifically or militarily important and angry at itself for having believed in the myth of American superiority. It was a time of intense reappraisal.

President Eisenhower reacted by calling in his Defense Department experts and asking them where the United States stood in regard to space. He was presented with the nose cone from a ballistic rocket that had withstood the fiery temperatures of re-entry. In a speech memorable for smugness, he pointed proudly to the nose cone as evidence that the U.S. was not far behind the U.S.S.R. This was a long way from the truth. A month before Sputnik I was launched, the Soviets had put a full-scale intercontinental ballistic missile through a very successful test. The ballistic rocket that boosted the President's nose cone was capable of delivering only the most minor of warheads. The military was aware of this, and so was Congress.

Nevertheless, Senators Lyndon Johnson, Styles Bridges, and Richard Russell were invited to the Pentagon for a briefing and were reassured that the Soviet success was a fluke and that our 3½-pound Vanguard satellite would soon fly. The briefing had barely ended when the Soviets rocketed the space dog Laika into orbit in a spaceship that weighed thousands of pounds and was plainly visible to U.S. citizens at certain times of the night.

Senator Lyndon Johnson was far from satisfied at the Administration's cavalier attitude toward space and ordered his Preparedness Investigating Subcommittee to hold open, formal hearings to determine the significance of the Soviet superiority in space. Moving with unusual speed, the subcommittee began hearings on November 25, 1957. The hearings lasted for weeks and were perhaps the most dramatic congressional hearings that had taken place since the Army-McCarthy hearings in the early 1950's. In one session, General James Gavin, in tears, described the army's frustration at being prevented from developing ballistic rockets. Senator Johnson's subcommittee hammered home the idea that the future of science and of the country's defense depended on space.

In December Senator Johnson announced that he had every intention of seeing that a civilian space agency was established within the coming months. In phone calls and meetings, however, Eisenhower continually questioned the relevance of space to defense and science. Using the persuasive techniques for which he was famous, Johnson finally succeeded in urging the reticent Chief Executive to cooperate. In February, 1958, the Advanced Research Projects Agency was created, making the Secretary of Defense responsible for space projects for one year. To Senate-watchers this was the tip-off that the space program would not be a long-term project for the Department of Defense.

On February 7, 1958, just six days after the United States

orbited Explorer I, Senator Johnson introduced, and the Senate passed the next day, a resolution establishing a committee with a somewhat redundant title—Special Committee on Space and Astronautics. The committee had thirteen members, seven Democrats and six Republicans.

For a while it had seemed as if every senator wanted to bring space under the jurisdiction of his own committee. One senator went so far as to propose that space should be the responsibility of the Committee on Commerce because of its communications potential. In a brilliant parliamentary move, Senator Johnson solved the whole problem by appointing all such committee chairmen to the new blue-ribbon committee. It was this action, as well as his hammering home of the significance of the initial Soviet successes in space, that many historians cite as Johnson's chief accomplishment as a Senate leader.

Still not too concerned with space, President Eisenhower made a formal proposal to Congress for a civilian space agency, "by request" from Senators Johnson and Bridges. ("By request" implies that a bill has been introduced on behalf of a senator—or by a senator on behalf of the President—as an act of courtesy. Frequently a senator will introduce a bill, by request, without having any intention of voting for it when it reaches the floor.)

The President's proposal did have one outstanding feature: the new space agency would be exclusively a civilian agency. Otherwise it was largely a name change for NACA. Many congressmen and senators were displeased with the proposal, feeling that it was totally inadequate to the national need. Under the Eisenhower formula, the director of the new agency could succeed only if other agencies were willing to cooperate.

Congress was disgruntled. It was the Army's Wernher von Braun who kept their faith by keeping his promise of putting a satellite into orbit within ninety days of a go-ahead order.

Von Braun, the Senate learned, had been prepared for over a year to put a satellite into orbit but, by order of the President, had had to defer to the Navy's civilian Vanguard project. He had saved several Redstone rockets and enough satellite hardware from his nose cone research program for just such an effort, but he had no desire to be transferred to a civilian agency. Von Braun believed that under Eisenhower a civilian agency would receive little money and that only the military could expect the enormous sums that would be needed to explore space.

CONGRESSIONAL ACTION

The House of Representatives did not get into the debate on space until Representative Carl Durham, chairman of the Joint Committee on Atomic Energy, announced that he was ordering the formation of a special Senate Subcommittee on Outer Space Propulsion, with Senator Clinton Anderson as its chairman. In January of 1958, hearings were held in executive session (closed to the public), at which many of the nation's space experts presented testimony.

During this same period, hundreds of bills were introduced in the Senate and the House, which would have divided responsibility for the space program in as many ways. The Subcommittee on Outer Space Propulsion proved to be abortive upon creation of Senator Lyndon Johnson's Special Committee on Space and Astronautics. Senator Clinton Anderson became a member of the new committee. On March 5, 1958, the House followed suit and established the Select Committee on Astronautics and Space Exploration with Congressman John W. McCormack as chairman. This body served as an interim committee in the months between the Sputnik crisis and the establishment of the National Aeronautics and Space Administration.

The Administration bill to create NASA was introduced

in the Senate on April 14, 1958, by Senators Johnson and Bridges and in the House by Representative McCormack. An adjustment made in the Senate version provided for the establishment of a National Aeronautics and Space Policy Board consisting of most Cabinet officers, the NASA Administrator, and the President, as chairman. Eisenhower let it be known that he had no stomach for such a board.* The House wanted more control over interagency relations. To fill this need it wanted a committee on defense and another on atomic energy rather than a policy board to settle disputes and promote projects. Senator Johnson was disgusted with the attitudes of both the White House and the House of Representatives. A compromise bill was finally voted into law on July 16, 1958. President Eisenhower, mindful of public opinion, signed the bill on July 29, 1958.

CONGRESSIONAL COMMITTEES

The Congress still had one major task ahead—how to handle legislation concerning the new agency. On July 15, 1958, Senator Lyndon Johnson introduced a resolution creating the Senate Committee on Aeronautical and Space Sciences. Most members of the Special Committee on Space and Aeronautics became members of the new standing committee. Johnson was made chairman. The House, after considering a Joint Committee on Space along the lines of the all-powerful Joint Committee on Atomic Energy, created the Committee

* Bryce Harlow, an Eisenhower aide, acted as Administration spokesman in this matter. Harlow, particularly, did not like the idea of a policy board. After a series of compromises, the proposed National Aeronautics and Space Policy Board became the National Aeronautics and Space Council, whose functions were merely advisory. Eisenhower angered Johnson by ignoring the board when the 1958 bill was passed. He failed to appoint an executive secretary to the council and in January, 1960, during the last days of his Administration, made the mistake of sending legislation to the Senate that would have abolished the council altogether. The bill was never put on the calendar.

on Science and Astronautics on July 21 to replace the Select Committee on Astronautics. Representative Overton Brooks of Louisiana was its first chairman.

The sixteen senators who presently sit on the Senate Committee on Aeronautical and Space Sciences work as a unit. Unlike the House Committee on Science and Astronautics, the Senate committee has no formal subcommittees. Staff work is vital to its functioning. Work assignments directed to perhaps one or two members come directly from the chairman. The committee has a professional staff of five, compared to the seventeen professional staff members of the House committee. The staffs of both committees conduct research to ensure that committee members have the information they need to make informed votes on NASA authorizations. NASA cooperates through its Office of Legislative Affairs, which provides witnesses, gathers testimony and facts, and arranges tours of NASA facilities for representatives and senators.

In recent years, meetings of the Senate Committee on Aeronautical and Space Sciences have provided a forum for NASA's critics. This open operation has not hindered NASA or the committee, but has actually increased its credibility.

Twenty-nine Congressmen make up the House Committee on Science and Astronautics. The chairman and the ranking minority member serve as ex-officio members of six subcommittees.

The *Subcommittee on Manned Space Flight* prepares and reviews legislation concerning all manned NASA operations. The *Subcommittee on Space Science and Applications* handles legislation and information pertaining to unmanned flight and useful applications of space information in general. The *Subcommittee on Aeronautics and Space Technology* is, along with the *Subcommittee on Science, Research and Development*, interested in various field center operations, research and development, and other areas pertaining directly to the area of flight preparation and research. The *Subcommittee on*

NASA Oversight sounds more fearful than it is. This eight-member group examines areas where NASA may have problems or potential problems and brings them to the attention of Congress. It also reviews all NASA authorizations. Similar congressional committees have traditionally been used to "lynch" the agencies involved, sometimes on rather flimsy evidence. To the credit of the House of Representatives, this has seldom been the case with the Subcommittee on NASA Oversight. The *Subcommittee on International Cooperation in Science and Space* is beginning to function in a very major way as it prepares for the joint U.S.-Soviet flight planned for the mid-1970's. All of the House subcommittees work together on legislation that covers a cross-section of NASA interests.

The legislative process is complicated. Contractors, as well as NASA itself, lobby for funds. Bitterness sometimes comes to the surface when a contractor loses a bid and the congressman representing the losing bidder brings the battle to the floor. Frequently legislation requires NASA to do things that it would prefer not to do. NASA balked at legislation requiring the Apollo missions to place American flags on the moon. The agency felt that such displays of nationalism did nothing to further the cause of peace and that every nation was well aware that it was the U.S. astronauts landing on the moon. When appropriations were tied to the legislation, NASA had no alternative but to back down.

Congress regards NASA as its own child, not without justification. During the 1960's, many military leaders looked on NASA's large budgets with regret, convinced that it had been a mistake to allow the space program to slip from the control of the Pentagon. Congressmen like the late L. Mendel Rivers constantly sought to bring space flight programs into the Pentagon, but to little avail. NASA was established as a civilian agency, and its stature in Congress was strong enough to withstand the bitterest of foes.

Yet, starting in 1968, NASA began receiving its smallest budgets since the Apollo program was announced. The pressures of the Vietnam War and disenchantment with the agency over the Apollo 204 fire were partly to blame. However, the underlying motivation behind the relatively austere budgets was the fact that hardware expenditures for Apollo were beginning to lessen. The 1968 budget cut marked the end of NASA's "high roller" days as an agency. Subsequent cuts paved the way for the 1970's, which promises to be the most austere period the young agency has gone through.

VIII

NASA and
Other Government Agencies

NASA's Office of Department of Defense and Interagency Affairs coordinates the space agency's relations with the rest of the federal establishment. The very title of this office indicates a top-heavy emphasis on relations with the Department of Defense. The reasons for this are many, stemming in part from the legislative history of NASA. The overwhelming reason, however, for NASA's reliance on the Defense Department first, and on other agencies secondarily, is an operational one.

In the days of the National Advisory Committee for Aeronautics, the military had priorities in booster research. When NASA was created, it had to borrow many of its rocket scientists and facilities from the Department of Defense. When water landings were decided upon in the first three manned programs, it became clear that the Navy would have to be asked to provide NASA with a fleet of recovery ships and trained crews for projects Mercury, Gemini, and Apollo.

Launch facilities were also lacking in the early days. When military boosters were needed for a civilian manned flight effort, NASA was forced to make use of the Cape Kennedy Air Force Station. A practical partnership resulted from this need. To avoid duplication of facilities, NASA borrowed facilities and personnel from the Department of Defense. Perhaps the Defense Department's greatest contribution was the astronaut corps itself. It was fairly obvious that the men who had the greatest opportunity to qualify for NASA space flights had been trained by the military. John Glenn, for example, had been a Marine ace in Korea and held several records in jet-powered flight. A good many military officers who became astronauts never returned to their former services but simply retired while on loan to NASA.

As the Apollo program progressed, the role of the military diminished. Military launch facilities were no longer required, and military boosters were now too small and too imprecise for the tasks ahead. Titan, the last military booster used as a vehicle in the two-man Gemini orbital project of the mid-1960's, was not as tall as the first stage of the Saturn V moon rocket. The armed forces still provided Atlas military boosters for use with satellites, but the new sophisticated Atlas required for NASA launchings was far too cumbersome for military needs. These rockets, the center of the American nuclear arsenal, and only loaned to NASA, were now of use only to NASA. Nevertheless, Defense-NASA cooperation will continue. The re-usable space transportation system—the Space Shuttle (See Chapter XIII)—will depend in part on a water recovery, so the Department of Defense may well be called upon again. Currently, about 210 military personnel are assigned to NASA.

This has not been a one-way partnership. NASA has contributed to the solution of many technological problems related to ICBM launch systems and has assisted the Department of Defense in the packaging, launching, and follow-up phases of its own satellite programs.

During the early and mid-1960's, the military believed that it should have its own manned program. Defense Secretary Robert McNamara made the operational decision during the Kennedy Administration that manned flight would be the exclusive province of NASA, yet a few congressional committees and some generals and defense contractors managed to keep such programs as the Manned Orbiting Laboratory and Project Dynasoar within the realm of the military. When NASA did inherit the technology from these ill-fated programs, it found little use for it.

NASA AND THE DEPARTMENT OF DEFENSE TODAY

Today the Department of Defense assists NASA with its extensive tracking facilities, including the Air Force Eastern Test Range, the Space and Missile Test Center, the Air Force Satellite Control Facility, the Navy Pacific Missile Range, and the Army range at White Sands, New Mexico. NASA and the Department have worked together in a number of continuing projects aside from tracking and recovery. In the area of advanced liquid rocket technology, highly reliable engines have been developed for eventual use in conjunction with the Space Shuttle and the so-called Space Tug.

Many at NASA feel that the Defense Department's space research budget should be turned over to NASA, since much of the Department's research seems to duplicate NASA's efforts, such as the ill-fated Dynasoar project and the Air Force's Manned Orbiting Laboratory Project. Dynasoar was to have some of the characteristics of the Space Shuttle. It was canceled just before the Manned Orbiting Laboratory project was eliminated in 1968. Both programs cost in excess of a billion dollars and neither of them saw a launch. Because of the enormous sums that the military has expended on unsuccessful space programs, NASA tends to cringe whenever the Department of Defense receives additional appropriations from Congress for space research and development.

The Aeronautics and Astronautics Coordinating Board is the formal coordinating mechanism between NASA and the Department of Defense. The Board oversees major projects such as the Space Shuttle and attempts to prevent duplication of effort. In the area of lunar and planetary activities, the Army Corps of Engineers provides NASA with topographic and other maps for the Apollo program. The Corps of Engineers has also provided major assistance in the construction of every major launch facility at Cape Kennedy since 1961.

The Navy serves NASA through its Solar Radiation Monitoring Satellite Program, which detects flare-ups on the sun and alerts NASA to the existence of solar flares sending out radiation in amounts large enough to kill an Apollo crew in deep space. This program is an excellent example of how science provides valuable support to the manned exploration of space.

THE NATIONAL AERONAUTICS AND SPACE COUNCIL

The executive branch's official connecting link with NASA is the National Aeronautics and Space Council, which was set up in 1958 to advise and assist the President in space matters. The Vice-President is the chairman of the Council and other members are the secretaries of State, Defense, and Transportation, the Administrator of NASA, and the chairman of the Atomic Energy Commission. The Secretary of Transportation was not an original member, but was added to the Council in the fall of 1970.

Formal meetings are held to discuss policy and to present the interests of various agencies in space-related activities. Informal council meetings are frequently held with only one or two Council members and their highly expert staffs, who assist in preparing recommendations that often lead to programs. The executive secretary of the council is a member of the National Security Council subcommittees that review and recommend projects and ideas involving international space cooperation.

The National Aeronautics and Space Council was not used

as a tool by the President until the Kennedy Administration. Early in the 1960 Presidential campaign, John Kennedy asked a group of experts, whom he had gathered as an *ad hoc* committee on space, for a report on where the United States stood and what our future policy should be. Their report caused Kennedy to conclude that the current national program had made far too small a commitment. Realizing that Lyndon Johnson, his candidate for Vice-President, was very much interested in the program, the President told Johnson that the program would be the main duty of Johnson's term of office. As Vice-President, Johnson ran the council and made it a valuable tool in determining space policy. Meetings and travels with the council staff enabled Johnson to formulate an idea of the nation's space capability. While he was in the process of doing this, he received the following memo that helped put the space program in high gear and changed Project Apollo into a lunar landing program.

April 20, 1961

MEMORANDUM FOR THE VICE PRESIDENT

In accordance with our conversation I would like for you as Chairman of the Space Council to be in charge of making an overall survey of where we stand in space.

1. Do we have a chance of beating the Soviets by putting a laboratory in space, or by a trip around the moon, or by a rocket to land on the moon, or by a rocket to go to the moon and back with a man. Is there any other space program which promises dramatic results in which we could win?
2. How much additional would it cost?
3. Are we working 24 hours a day on existing programs. If not, why not? If not, will you make recommendations to me as how work can be speeded up?
4. In building large boosters should we put our emphasis on nuclear, chemical, or liquid fuel, or a combination of these three?

5. Are we making maximum effort? Are we achieving necessary results?

I have asked Jim Webb, Dr. Wiesner, Secretary McNamara and other responsible officials to cooperate with you fully. I would appreciate a report on this at the earliest possible moment.

JOHN F. KENNEDY

As Presidential Administrations changed, so did the leadership of the National Aeronautics and Space Council—and its effectiveness in making policy determinations. When Lyndon Johnson's Vice-President, Hubert Humphrey, was chairman of the council, its importance in decision-making continued. President Nixon often preferred the opinions of his own aides to those of the council's professional staff, which represents a cross-section of bureaucratic opinion. In Vice-President Spiro Agnew, the council gained a highly enthusiastic champion, but also a chairman who spoke too soon. His statements concerning a Mars landing after the Apollo 11 lift-off damaged both the council's and his own reputation.

THE ATOMIC ENERGY COMMISSION

The two major areas of Atomic Energy Commission and NASA cooperation are nuclear rocket development, on which long-range flights now depend, and the development of power generators for our most sophisticated space missions, such as the so-called Grand Tour envisioned for the end of the 1970 decade.

The "SNAP" generators developed by the AEC have provided electric power for all Apollo scientific instrument packages. The generators used on the moon are of a decaying heat source type, which provides for the generation of power over long periods of time. In addition to ground-based generating systems, on-board systems for manned craft are under study. Since the SNAP cannister stored in the lunar module contains plutonium and could be highly dangerous if a launch pad abort occurs, an AEC expert is on hand at Cape Kennedy during launchings to oversee recovery of the plutonium under the safest possible conditions, and the casing around the reactor will have already been tested under launch-abort conditions. The generator on Apollo 13 landed intact in the Pacific, and the cannister gave no evidence of leakage.

Since nuclear power systems weigh less than solar or battery systems, NASA's Pioneer probe to Jupiter will be powered by a SNAP generator. The light weight allows for a greater number of on-board experiments. The Mars probe Viking will also use a SNAP generator. Isotopic space power systems for journeys to the outer planets are under development. System modules will produce from 100 to 1,000 watts of power and serve as building blocks for larger systems.

The goal of the joint NASA/AEC Nuclear Rocket Program has been to develop NERVA (Nuclear Engine for Rocket Vehicle Application). NERVA is a 75,000-pound upper-stage engine designed for long-range space flight. The benefits of such a project are discussed in a later chapter, but the research work is nearly complete, and tests have shown that the system is ready for a tryout in space. The technology for an upper stage is available. Most scientists agree that this is the only possible way to attempt a Mars flight. Budget constraints on both agencies have temporarily shelved the program, however, and the giant rocket development station at the Nevada test site is now closed down.

DEPARTMENT OF STATE

In accordance with the Department of State's role under the National Aeronautics and Space Act, the United States has made space an instrument of foreign policy. The role of the State Department in space ranges from the arranging of tours of astronauts to joint space efforts with other nations. The State Department coordinates these activities, as well as similar activities within the United Nations. It assists and advises NASA on bilateral agreements and provides support for more difficult agreements in such areas as U.S.-Soviet cooperation.

The State Department is responsible for obtaining foreign cooperation during manned flight emergencies. If an emergency made a landing in another part of the world necessary, for example, the State Department would make all the arrangements. During the Apollo 13 emergency, the State Department cleared world radio frequencies during the final phase of the re-entry and landing process.

The State Department's Undersecretary for Political Affairs has assisted NASA in funneling requests for experiments in the Skylab program from foreign scientists and has obtained assurance of protection of post-Apollo technical data released by NASA.

In 1964 agreements were signed creating the International Telecommunications Satellite Consortium (Intelsat), and in 1969 the United States began to make plans and definite arrangements to implement the system. Intelsat now has a membership of almost eighty nations. The State Department assisted in the arrangements for Intelsat meetings and documents. It also helped NASA make arrangements for cooperative use of Air Traffic Control Satellites.

In the area of meteorological satellites, the State Department has worked with the World Meteorological Organization in the development of the Global Atmospheric Research Program. This program will use four satellites. Two will be launched by NASA, one by France, and one may be launched by Japan. The State Department also participated in the successful National Geodetic Satellite Program, which mapped the world's oceans. Twenty-eight nations were involved in the program.

DEPARTMENT OF TRANSPORTATION

One of the most important cooperative efforts between NASA and the Department of Transportation is the Civil Aviation Research and Development Policy Study. This is a complete overview of civil aviation and how the United States can keep its lead in the field. NASA and the Department have also been working on air traffic control satellites. Research in oceanic traffic control is also under way.

Responsibility for NASA's once enormous electronics research center in Cambridge, Massachusetts, was transferred to the Department of Transportation in July, 1970. The organization at Cambridge was re-oriented and its contribution to the transportation field has begun to demonstrate itself.

The Department's Federal Aviation Administration is working with NASA in numerous aeronautical research activities. Short take-off and landing vehicles, the supercritical wing, and the Space Shuttle are being studied jointly by the two agencies.

DEPARTMENT OF THE INTERIOR

The Department of the Interior has long worked with NASA in making observations of natural resources from space. Support has been given to NASA by the Department in lunar mapping, analysis of lunar materials, the development of lunar landing sample programs, life-support systems for spacecraft, and the calibration of equipment for the Earth Resources Technology Satellite (ERTS) Program. The Department of the Interior is assisting NASA in a dry run of the first ERTS satellite launch and has jointly prepared a data center with NASA in Sioux Falls, South Dakota. The center will process, disseminate, and store ERTS data for broad use throughout the world and make sure broadly applicable information is distributed. It will also provide facilities for user training and data use and develop methods to produce resource maps and statistics gathered from the ERTS satellites. The ERTS program is discussed more fully in Chapters XII and XIII.

The Department's Bureau of Mines is studying Gemini and Apollo photographs to determine the applications of space photography to large-scale mining operations. Its National Park Service is using Apollo 9 photography of the barrier islands of the United States to aid in management of the area. The Saguarro National Monument near Tucson, Arizona, needs new roads, and the Park Service is using Gemini and Apollo photographs to determine the placement of the roads.

The U.S. Geological Survey, also in Interior, has been working with NASA on projects ranging from mosaic mapping of the United States to mapping the moon with Lunar Orbiter IV. The two agencies are involved in a variety of international activities, ranging from the reclamation of the Pa Mong area in Thailand and Laos to a study of the geothermal conditions of Lake Chapala in Mexico.

DEPARTMENT OF AGRICULTURE

The Department of Agriculture and NASA are involved in a remote sensing program of earth resources such as soils, forests, and crops. The Department will collect and disseminate data from NASA's Earth Resources Technology Satellites. Thanks to this program, a worldwide system will be able to detect soil fatigue several years in advance and thus control potential problems. The remote sensing program of the Skylab space station should save billions of dollars a year by predicting crop disasters so that countermeasures can be taken before disaster strikes.

DEPARTMENT OF COMMERCE

The National Oceanic and Atmospheric Administration of the Department of Commerce was created to chart the oceans and tc learn all there is to know about them. It also has the responsibility of predicting the changes in all elements of the environment in real time. The atmosphere, the oceans, and the solid earth will all be under constant surveillance.

To aid in this enormous job, NASA has launched a growing family of satellites to do the necessary work of monitoring the earth and providing a total weather satellite system. The National Weather Service is involved in the space program in two ways. First, it provides weather support for NASA launches. Second, it studies space technology to be able to communicate weather information quickly. The series of Applications and Technology Satellites (ATS) are used to measure river-stages and rainfall by collecting data from automatic stations and relaying them to a central station. Hydrologists will eventually have the benefit of satellites for snow mapping, and thus be able to determine water supply for certain areas when the spring rains come. In addition, valuable information about flood control can be obtained.

The National Marine Fisheries Service will use remote sensing to follow the activating of marine life. The Earth Resources Technology Satellite and Skylab programs will carry infrared equipment to provide surface temperatures and other infrared data with regard to marine life. The various environmental labs of the Commerce Department also actively work with NASA in exploring and improving the environment.

Commerce's National Bureau of Standards is involved in numerous activities with NASA, mostly of a highly scientific nature. Two members of the Bureau of Standards staff assisted in the Apollo 13 accident investigation. Other Department of Commerce units have conducted experiments for NASA, ranging from the simulation of lunar samples to investigations of failures in satellite tape recorders.

Department of Commerce activities in cooperation with NASA are the most extensive of any governmental agency and have affected more people than any other cooperative NASA projects.

NATIONAL ACADEMY OF SCIENCES–NATIONAL ACADEMY OF ENGINEERING–NATIONAL RESEARCH COUNCIL

The National Academy of Sciences in Washington, D.C., is asked to conduct reviews of various NASA programs from time to time to determine whether they are meeting the objectives for which they were originally established. The Academy also puts out reports and recommendations that lead to actual exploration programs and to new thinking in terms of space.

The Space Science Board of the National Research Council is the principal scientific advisory group on the direction of the space program in this country. It represents the National Academy of Sciences on the International Committee on Space Research and discusses space objectives with officials of NASA and other interested agencies. The board's views are made known each year in time to be included in budget planning by agency heads.

The Space Science Board is also highly interested in promoting world interest in space research. It works with NASA in disseminating information at world scientific forums.

The National Research Council offers research to NASA in a variety of important areas. The Division of Behavioral Sciences is investigating long-range space flight and its physical and other effects. The Division of Earth Sciences assists NASA in the Earth Resources Technology Satellites as well as in the Applications Technology Satellites. The Division of Engineering and its Materials Advisory Board suggest materials for space flight and improvements on construction techniques. The Division of Physical Sciences assists NASA by suggesting experiments for missions ranging from sounding rockets to orbital craft. The Office of Scientific Personnel administers the NASA International University Fellowship program and the NASA Postdoctoral and Senior Postdoctoral Resident Research Associateship Programs. More than three hundred fellowships have been awarded under the program since 1961.

OTHER AGENCIES

The Smithsonian Institution has been concerned with manned flight for almost a century. Smithsonian scientists are deeply involved in studying lunar samples from the Apollo program. Under the terms of the Space Artifacts Agreement with NASA, the Institution collects such artifacts as space capsules, space suits, and other equipment and exhibits these items on tours throughout the country and around the world. A National Air and Space Museum has long been envisioned for Washington, D.C., and land is available although money is not. Currently the collection is housed in a temporary building and in the aging Smithsonian Arts and Industries Building on the Mall, where many small rockets from the early space program have been put on outdoor display. The collection includes a forty-foot scale model of the Saturn V moon booster and the Apollo 11 command module. Most of the unexhibited and unrestored collection is stored at Silver Hill, Maryland—thousands of tons of space equipment, waiting for the day when a building will be built to house the vast collection.

The Federal Communications Commission is involved with NASA in several ways. It has specific responsibilities for the communications satellites orbited by the United States. It is in charge of national and international participation in, and arrangements for, the aviation, marine, and weather uses of such satellites. The Commission administers rules and regulations regarding nongovernmental radio communications and participates in national and international frequency allocations and in solving technical, operational, and policy problems relating to aeronautical communications, space satellites, and radio astronomy.

The Intelsat satellite system is now using almost 3,000 circuits. This global satellite system has more than forty earth stations operating in thirty different nations. This increase in communications activities has put heavy responsibility on the Federal Communications Commission. That agency has been working with the airlines and with NASA to test the feasibility of using the Applications Technology Satellites as prototypes of satellites for an air traffic control system.

The Arms Control and Disarmament Agency made it possible for the United States to move ahead in space under the Outer Space Treaty. More than sixty governments have subscribed to the treaty, which bans nuclear weapons from space. In the area of space cooperation, the Agency is responsible for seeing that equipment transferred for such international efforts is used for the designated purpose and not channeled to the military.

The National Science Foundation sees that NASA includes the maximum number of scientific experiments on each of its missions. The Foundation works with NASA on assisting foreign space scientists and disseminating information. The Foundation also provides support for NASA in engineering and astronomy.

NASA has maintained an informal relationship with all of the above government agencies in the exchange of specialized services. Its frequent requests for advice are mostly informal. Cooperation between NASA and sometimes competing agencies has been rather remarkable. The Department of Defense, which failed so miserably because of interservice disputes over space activities in the 1950's, has established a sound record of cooperation with the civilian agency. The relationship between NASA and the other civilian agencies has been one of success in the utilization of tax dollars. In addition to the lunar landing, the American people have realized a series of very practical benefits, many made possible in part by the relationships NASA has developed with the rest of the federal government.

In NASA's first decade, the Department of Defense has dominated the interagency picture. With the advent of various applications programs and the creation in 1971 of an Office of Space Applications, it seems as if the future will indicate a more even-handed approach by NASA to other agencies. In its early days, NASA looked to the Defense Department for help in getting started. Today NASA can provide a multitude of services for other civilian agencies, and future cross-governmental relations will be more broadly based.

IX

NASA and the World

The Space Act requires that this country's space activities "be devoted to peaceful purposes for the benefit of all mankind." The stated goals of NASA's international programs are, accordingly, the stimulation of space science on a worldwide scale, the enhancement of space experiments by ground support programs, the expansion of the number of competent scientists involved in space science, and the extension of the ties between national scientific communities.

To prevent confusion and controversy, NASA has set up guidelines for dealing with other nations. The first is that agreements will be made only with nations that have designated a central agency for the negotiation and supervision of joint projects. The second guideline is that agreements will concern specific projects rather than general programs. NASA also requires that a nation accept financial responsibility for its contribution to a joint project. This does not mean an equal sharing of cost but merely an agreement to meet obligations. Only projects of mutual scientific interest will be undertaken by NASA with another nation. The last and perhaps most important NASA guideline is that the scientific results of all cooperative efforts be made available to the world community.

NASA's cooperative projects form an impressive list, ranging from small sounding rockets to the Space Shuttle. Other important areas investigated jointly are meteorology, communications, ionospheric research, satellites, deep-space probes, instrumentation, and tracking. A summary of NASA's international activities, by country, will be found in Appendix B.

In March of 1959, the fledgling agency took what seemed to be in those days a giant step. It agreed to put payloads into space for other nations. On April 26, 1962, the United States and the United Kingdom launched the first international space payload—Ariel, designed to study electron temperatures and concentrations in the ionosphere. British scientists provided the experimental equipment; NASA designed and fabricated the structure. The second international satellite, Alouette, was launched on September 29, 1962, again to study the ionosphere. The satellite was funded and built by Canada; the United States supplied the Thor-Agena launch vehicle. NASA's most active international program—experimental sounding rockets—has involved such disparate countries as Sweden and Pakistan.

To encourage the work of foreign scientists in space research, NASA initiated an international fellowship program with eighteen American universities in September of 1961. Under this program, foreign graduate students are provided an opportunity for one to two years of study in the United States on a shared cost basis. NASA pays the tuition, laboratory costs, and travel in the United States, and the foreign government pays for travel to the U.S., subsistence, and expenses of dependents. The program is administered for NASA by the National Academy of Sciences. In addition, foreign technicians and scientists have been invited to NASA field centers in support of cooperative satellite and sounding-rocket programs and ground-facility operations. Training lasts from several months to a year. Thousands of foreign officials and scientists have visited NASA facilities, and NASA has used these visits to demonstrate not only the U.S. technical ability, but the openness of the U.S. space effort.

European countries take a dual approach to space. The larger nations maintain strong national programs, and the smaller nations join the larger nations in membership in several regional organizations. The European Launcher Development Organization (ELDO) and the European Space Research Organization (ESRO) were both formed to permit European governments to pool their efforts in larger space efforts than would otherwise be possible.

ELDO has for years been attempting to develop an Atlas-class launch vehicle to boost ESRO-researched packages into space, but, as in the case of the Concorde supersonic transport, things have not gone well.

Membership in ELDO includes the United Kingdom, France, West Germany, Italy, Belgium, the Netherlands, and Australia. Their effort to develop a launcher has met with failures and delays, despite which the organization has refused American offers to sell nonmilitary versions of a variety of booster rockets.

ESRO, responsible for engineering of satellites and probes, a twelve-member organization, includes the United Kingdom, France, Germany, Italy, the Netherlands, Belgium, Switzerland, Austria, Sweden, Spain, Denmark, and Norway. It was established to help provide facilities for participating nations to carry out space research, but not as an organization conducting space research in its own right.

NASA AND THE U.S.S.R.

On October 12, 1962, an agreement was signed by the United States and the Soviet Union for a joint space effort in telecommunications, meteorology, and a worldwide geomagnetic survey. The year 1963 was to be used for setting up data links and designing experiments, and 1964 for the operational phase. Hopes for the 1962 agreement were high, but the Soviet performance was disappointing. By the end of 1972, only the communications project had been completed. The Soviet Union refused to transmit but did provide reasonable information regarding radio reception from space.

Since the 1962 agreement was signed, the U.S. has made the following offers to the Soviets:

September 20, 1962. In a speech to the United Nations General Assembly, President Kennedy suggested that the U.S. and the Soviet Union join in the lunar landing. Later, President Johnson reaffirmed this offer, but no Soviet response was ever received.

December 8, 1964. NASA proposed an exchange of visits by U.S. and Soviet teams to facilities for deep-space tracking and data acquisition. The Soviets replied on August 13, 1965, that such visits were not then possible.

May 3, 1965. NASA suggested a U.S.-Soviet communications test via the Soviet satellite Molniya I. There was no Soviet response.

August 25, 1965. At the request of President Johnson, NASA Administrator James Webb invited the Soviet Academy of Sciences to send a high-level representative to the launching of Gemini VI. At the same time the President announced that he would welcome joint exploration with the Soviets. The Soviets did not accept either invitation.

November 16, 1965. NASA again asked the Soviets about tests via Molniya I. On January 23, 1966, the Soviets answered that such tests were not possible "in the recent conditions."

January 6, 1966. Administrator Webb asked Academician Blagonravov, Chairman of the Soviet Academy of Science's Commission on the Exploration and Use of Outer Space, for a description of experiments on Soviet Venus probes so that the U.S. might fly experiments that would complement rather than compete with the Soviet probes. Blagonravov replied informally that he did not have the authority to provide Webb with such material.

March 24 and May 23, 1966. Administrator Webb suggested to Academician Blagonravov that the Soviets suggest subjects for discussion with a view to extending cooperation between NASA and the Soviet Academy. Blagonravov replied, again informally, that his country was not ready for such cooperation.

September 22, 1966. United Nations Ambassador Arthur Goldberg offered the Soviets U.S. territorial tracking coverage if they desired it.

On March 27, 1967, the ice was finally broken when Frederick Seitz, president of the National Academy of Sciences, proposed to M. V. Keldysh, president of the U.S.S.R. Academy of Sciences, that they provide the United States with results of soil tests of Luna 13 in return for the data from U.S. Surveyor flights. President Keldysh forwarded some data, but it was not until the U.S. lunar landing in 1969 that the real thaw began. With the race for the moon over, the Soviets were apparently ready to at least talk, and on October 28, 1970, an agreement was signed in Moscow to establish working groups to discuss joint space ventures.

Avoiding the premature euphoria that followed the 1962 agreement, officials at the Manned Spacecraft Center near Houston hosted the working sessions held from June 21 to 25, 1971, concerned with hardware development for joint flights. Further meetings have been held, and a joint mission can be expected sometime in the 1970's. As an aftermath of the 1971 meetings, the way was cleared for a joint study of U.S. lunar samples and an exchange of information on the Soviet Mars probes and the highly successful U.S. Mariner 9 probe of the same planet.

Sharing technology with the Soviets is difficult, due to the fact that the Soviet civilian space effort is integrated with the military program. Recently, the Soviets have taken a more cooperative position with regard to the East European nations. With the Soviets now working with NASA on joint manned missions, it can be expected that they will play an active role in international space exploration in the future.

THE UNITED NATIONS

Space cooperation within the United Nations comes under the jurisdiction of the U.N. General Assembly. Areas of cooperation identified by the General Assembly include general legal principles to ensure that space will be used for peaceful purposes, scientific research, weather satellites and meteorology, and training and education. While some of these areas come within the province of standing U.N. committees, it was decided to direct the over-all space program from the Committee on the Peaceful Uses of Outer Space. This committee held its first meeting in March of 1962 and established two subcommittees, one to deal with legal matters and the other with technical and scientific cooperation. The committee and its subcommittee have been assisted by the U.S. State Department in a variety of areas. One of the most interesting problems dealt with was a treaty to fix liability when damage is caused by objects returning from outer space or during an abortive mission. The committee's Scientific and Technical Subcommittee has been working with NASA and the State Department in programs involving NASA's Earth Resources Satellites and Applications Technology Satellites.

The United Nations has passed a number of important resolutions pertaining to space. On December 20, 1961, the U.N. adopted a resolution that extended the coverage of its Charter so as to include outer space. This resolution also called for a global communications satellite system and required U.N. members to list all satellite and space probe launches in a central registry. The U.S. and the U.S.S.R. have supplied the registry with such information as purpose of the satellite, name of the booster, orbital parameters, and launch data. The U.N.'s World Meteorological Organization was ordered by the General Assembly to draw up proposals for an international weather service program in cooperation with the United Nations Educational, Scientific, and Cultural Organization. The International Telecommunications Union was assigned the role of assisting in a global communications system.

The 1960's saw NASA developing cooperative efforts with 70 countries. Almost 250 agreements with other nations provided the basis for this work. By the end of the decade, 50 countries were receiving weather information from U.S. satellites, and some 500 sounding-rocket experiments had been carried out.

INTERNATIONAL SCIENTIFIC ORGANIZATIONS

NASA cooperates with the following nongovernment international organizations.

The International Council of Scientific Unions (ICSU) is composed of fourteen international scientific unions and more than forty national scientific institutions representing as many nations. Each of the fourteen unions is devoted to a discipline of science ranging from astronomy to physiology.

The Committee on Space Research (COSPAR) was established in 1958 by the General Assembly of the International Council of Scientific Unions. (Nine of the Council's scientific unions currently participate.) The function of COSPAR is to exchange data on an international basis. It has established several working groups to formulate procedures for specific efforts. They include working groups on tracking and transmission, on scientific experiments, on data and publications, and, lastly, a special working group on the effects of nuclear testing on space.

The International Astronautical Federation (IAF) was

founded at the 1950 International Astronautical Congress by members of the national academies of nations interested in rocketry and the development of interplanetary flight. The Federation has a Permanent Legal Committee, a Committee on International Cooperation, and several other active committees.

INTERNATIONAL PROGRAMS

The first major international space undertaking was the Telstar demonstration of 1962. A signal was sent from a ground station in France up to the Telstar satellite and back to the American Telephone and Telegraph Station at Andover, Maine, from which it was transmitted to millions of U.S. television screens. It was a revelation to the United States and Europe—the first "spinoff" from the young space program. Since then, major ground stations have been established by NASA in a dozen countries for the testing of communications satellites.

NASA's argument for a heavier program of international work in the 1970's was made by former NASA Administrator Thomas Paine when he addressed the Senate Committee on Aeronautical and Space Sciences in March of 1970:

These projects, together with a wide range of work still under-way, are bringing very real benefits to the United States and her cooperating partners.

There are significant cost savings, for example, when Canada assumes responsibility for a series of satellites in the NASA ionospheric research program, when Germany undertakes a major solar probe program with us, and when countries such as Brazil, India, and Norway provide extensive range support for sounding-rocket projects which require their unique geographic locations.

There are rich scientific benefits when gifted foreign experi-menters win opportunities to fly instruments on NASA satellites after vigorous competitive selection.

I am confident also that the Nation and the World are deriving important intangible benefits—political benefits, if you will—from the open and peaceful U.S. program.

Outside of the Soviet Union and the United States, numerous countries are involved in space on a much smaller scale. Over $100 million of the more than $300 million of such activities goes to the regional partnerships, ESRO and ELDO, described above. The remaining funds are used by West Germany, France, Britain, Canada, and Italy for satellites developed for launching by NASA, usually on a cooperative, but occasionally on a reimbursable, basis.

France. In the late 1960's it appeared as if France, which had used its own booster to launch a satellite, would be the space leader among the third world countries. France has developed a Diamant V booster capable of placing 300 pounds in near-earth orbit. France is stressing applications satellites such as Symphonic, a project undertaken with West Germany. The French have space laboratories at Paris and Toulouse and the Guiana range and have established a tracking and data acquisition network that compares favorably to that of the United States. Cooperation between NASA and the French space agency has been extensive. A French satellite was launched by NASA in 1965. A synchronous weather satellite is in the works, and an agreement to use the French tracking system in exchange for use of the NASA system has been reached.

Brazil. Brazil carries out a very active program under the direction of the Brazilian Space Commission. NASA and Brazil have undertaken numerous sounding-rocket experiments including those that would lead to a weather satellite system for Latin America. Experiments with U.S. Applications Technology Satellites will be made over Brazil, and earth resources surveys will be conducted from NASA planes and later from Earth Resources Technology Satellites.

Canada. Canada's primary interest in space is in solving the difficulties of communicating near and through the polar ionosphere. This led Canada to join with NASA in 1962, early in the international program. The Canadian-built Alouette Satellites have contributed greatly to the U.S. space effort. Canada is developing a communications system and will purchase NASA launchings for the project. NASA has used the Canadian Black Brant Rocket for its own sounding-rocket experiments. The Canadians use the Churchill Rocket Research Range in the auroral zone.

West Germany. After a slow start, the funding of the West German program now exceeds that of France. German programs are mostly joint efforts with the United States or with European partners. AZUR I, the first German satellite, was launched by NASA in 1969. The most exciting joint project is Helios, which will take seven German and three U.S. experiment packages closer to the sun than any other spacecraft in history. This is the largest and most complex project undertaken outside the U.S. and Soviet national programs. Germany has played a leading role in both the European Space Research Organization and the European Launcher Development Organization and has been responsible for the management of the so far ill-fated launch vehicle of the last-named organization. The Germans have also made enormous investments in testing facilities and laboratories.

India. India has been working with NASA on numerous sounding-rocket experiments. The Indian launch facility at Thumba was accorded U.N. sponsorship in 1965. India now builds its own sounding rockets in a foreign-owned factory and has a small rocket capability of its own, which it plans to scale up to satellite launching size by the mid-1970's. The most important Indian project will be sponsored by India's Department of Atomic Energy and will use a U.S. Applications Technology Satellite in an experimental direct broadcast made to some 5,000 remote Indian villages.

Italy. The Italian program has been centered on the San Marco satellite program for measuring atmospheric density by means of a satellite placed directly in equatorial orbit from a mobile platform in the Indian Ocean off the coast of Kenya. NASA provided several Scout vehicles for these launches, and Italy has agreed to launch a number of U.S. projects from their platform at cost. Italy is also developing several projects for reimbursable launching by NASA in the 1970's.

Japan. In February, 1970, Japan became the fourth country to use its own launch vehicle to orbit a satellite, the Lambda 4 S. Success came after four failures beginning in 1966. Japan's limited funding may have contributed to the earlier failures. After the success of the Lambda 4 S, the Japanese increased spending for their space program several fold. The Japanese are also developing the Q and N rockets of much larger capacity than Lambda for communications satellite launches. A diplomatic-level agreement with the U.S. was reached in 1969 for the purchase of boosters from U.S. manufacturers, on the condition that Japan would not transfer the technology thus obtained to a third country and that her communications program would be compatible with Intelsat.

United Kingdom. Space funding in Great Britain has been limited to about $60 million a year. England's space activity is highly scientific in nature. The country has collaborated with both the United States and European countries in various projects. NASA has launched numerous British satellites, and Britain has had more experiments selected for flight by NASA than any other country. Seventeen of the fifty-five principal investigators for moon rock study are British. The United Kingdom developed the Blue Streak first-stage rocket for the European Launch Development Organization but withdrew from that organization because of the apparent lack of success of the booster. Britain has developed a small rocket called the Black Arrow designed to put 200 pounds into low-earth orbit.

In the 1960's, the United States spent $40 million on its international space activities as against approximately $200 million by collaborating countries. The reason for the difference in these amounts is economics. The United States, for the most part, provides boosters; most of these are not very large and are available right from the production line. Boosters, while expensive, cost far less than payloads because of the science and engineering involved in payload construction.

INTERNATIONAL COOPERATION

Individual space programs of small size can make only a fragmentary contribution when the cost of space exploitation is taken into account. Massive efforts to use space to assist mankind will depend on the pooling of funds, knowledge, and resources. Communications and weather satellites are a start, but, as political divisions and priorities stand today, peace-through-space is not in sight for the 1970's.

If numbers of agreements were the sole criterion, the United States' space record on the international front would indeed be impressive. Some 25 nations have entered into cooperative space agreements with NASA; 73 nations are involved with ground-based programs; 39 have exchanged personnel; 21 nations are involved in tracking and data acquisition. All this is as nothing compared to areas in which there has been no cooperation.

Space technology today has the capability to prevent crop failures and to forestall weather disasters throughout the world, but resources are not equalized, and there is incredible duplication of effort and enormous waste. Only a massive effort to integrate all national space efforts will guarantee the fullest use of space to man. The technology of Europe and the Soviet Union could be pooled along with joint economic resources to reap a rewarding harvest. Separate programs mean that the United States and the Soviet Union will create essentially the same technology, spending time and money to reach the same goals by different routes.

The most interesting proposal now under discussion in the international aviation community is a revolutionary proposal, which, if adopted, would change the future of space for the world community. Many of the large American and European aerospace contractors are considering the idea of merging into consortiums to sell space transportation to whatever nation is willing to pay for it. Farfetched? Perhaps, but giant companies caught in national government budget restraints must seek other sources of revenue to keep their technology alive and in demand. If a joint American-Russian flight occurs, chances are the enactment of this proposal will act as a catalyst in dissolving bureaucratic timidity. In any event, economic realities will dictate the choice of one of three roads: full cooperation, superficial cooperation, or nationalistic progress. Which road is chosen depends not on national ego but on the realities all nations must face.

NASA has managed to avoid the military implications of joint cooperation, except on one occasion. On November 29, 1967, the agency launched a small satellite for the Weapons Research Establishment of the Australian Government. Under NASA guidelines, a central agency must be appointed by the cooperating government. Australia, planning no major program, merely assigned the project to the Weapons Research Establishment as a matter of bureaucratic routine, but Congress rose in anger, and, since that incident, NASA has paid more attention to the cooperating nations' semantics.

While the future appears clouded, NASA plans to continue its relatively inexpensive but rewarding international program on as big a scale as cutbacks will allow. Many critics of the human condition claim that duplication of effort is typical of mankind, but what a waste that the United States plans to send Viking to Mars while the Soviet Union plans a Martian program of its own.

Example after example of what joint planning could mean can be given. If all nations joined in development of the Space Shuttle Reusable Transportation System, for instance, it would mean that the $5.15 billion cost could be absorbed by a number of economies and the benefits from the system would accrue to many nations rather than only one. How costly it would be if the U.S., the Soviet Union, and the European countries engaged in a three-way effort to build different shuttle systems. A joint effort in a space station for practical earth resources study is also feasible. Billions could be saved if standardized docking systems, atmospheres, and other technical requirements for joint missions were established. Even in this era of tight budgets, a joint cosmonaut-astronaut training program would be possible.

One misconception that the United States and the Soviet Union will have to correct is that their superiority in spending on space does not mean that the rest of the world is devoid of ideas. A better effort to tap the scientific minds of other nations must be made. Japan has largely been left out of cooperative ventures. Although Europe has been preoccupied with the development of its own program, it has received inordinately more attention from both the United States and the Soviets than has any other part of the world.

If we fail to pool resources and combine overlapping programs, the chaos of today will be even worse tomorrow. The communications satellite system put up by the U.S. has been spectacularly successful, but a duplicate system is being orbited by the Soviet Union, and the Soviets, like us, have invested hundreds of millions of dollars in a skylab program. An even more compelling reason for international cooperation is that space, despite our treaties, can still be a military battleground, and the only insurance against clandestine development of space as an armed camp is a large, open, and cooperative space program.

"We came in peace for all mankind."

Those words were painted on the side of the lunar module left behind by the first Apollo astronauts to land on the moon. Unless we recognize the true economics of space exploration, unless we face political reality and resist the temptations of our national egos, those words will be as empty in meaning as the now rusted first-generation intercontinental ballistic missile sites that line the Great Plains of the United States and the Soviet Union.

X

The Information Program

During the early days at NASA, the public information people spent most of their time answering letters from citizens concerned about the United States being behind in space and trying to find out just what the public information policy in this new undertaking would be. Porter Brown, Mission Director for Skylab, the space station program, put it this way:

In those days everything was a mixture of security and public information. The press, prior to the manned launchings, was kept off the Cape. We used to go into town after a launch and hold a post flight briefing where we didn't say much. After all, the Atlas [Mercury booster] was still our number one ICBM, and the Air Force didn't have much use for us anyway, so we watched ourselves. On occasion the press would write a story that would paint a horrible picture, but because of security we could not even tell them what was going on. But as the program picked up and we got into the manned phase, things improved quickly.

Although over 400 correspondents were assigned to cover the suborbital flight of Alan Shepard in 1961, relations with the press were not good. The press was angry because it was allowed to view only the lift-off and was not permitted to have a representative in the blockhouse or in the control room. But as more money became available and as contractor public relations became more sophisticated, the situation improved. By the time the Gemini program ended, it was possible for the press to get almost any reasonable request fulfilled.

Despite printed statements to the contrary, NASA and the President were concerned with making the most of the early manned flights and the issue of openness.

THE UNITED STATES INFORMATION AGENCY

By Presidential directive, the United States Information Agency prepared numerous papers on the exploitative use of NASA. The first such paper, dated May 9, 1960, and entitled "A Program for USIA Exploitation of NASA Activities," set forth exactly what should be done to get the most out of each NASA program. The report recommended that the facilities at Wallops Island for launching Scout, a 70-foot booster used for small payloads, be turned into a center for international study—with the proviso that the facilities under no circumstances should be identified as a "plush" facility for foreigners but instead should be a reasonably comfortable NASA facility, "Spartan in appearance." The report further suggested that the Project Mercury vehicle carry a giant flashlight that could be seen easily by watchers on the ground. In the words of the memo: "For clear and ready identification of the orbiting capsule, a light of great intensity would be needed. The difficulties are appreciated; however, examination of the possibility would certainly be worthwhile." The report went on to suggest that NASA install a high-speed communications setup to inform cities when the light would be overhead.

The United States Information Agency report had President Dwight D. Eisenhower's hearty approval. He urged

NASA to undertake as many of the recommendations as possible to counteract the Soviet successes.

When President John F. Kennedy took office in 1961, he was very much concerned with NASA's image. Kennedy believed in an open space program of larger magnitude. With this in mind, the U.S. Information Agency prepared and released another report on May 18, 1961, entitled *Psychological Effects of Openness in U.S. Space Flight*. The report met the issue of a space race head on:

> The actual success of the flight [of Alan Shepard] revived popular anticipation that the space race would continue to show a general see-saw pattern, this thwarting for the time being a determined Soviet propaganda effort to foster the conclusion that Gagarin's flight meant the U.S. had irrevocably lost the space race. A second series of effects, perhaps even more significant over the long range, stems from the open public handling of the event.

President Kennedy constantly sought the most dramatic approach. He was determined to get the most mileage out of the idea that the United States was the underdog in space trying valiantly to catch up. He urged Vice-President Johnson to do his best to exploit the openness of the program and, wherever possible, to heighten the drama.

Because the job of the United States Information Agency is to tell America's story—and obviously the space program has been an important part of that story over the last decade—the Agency uses film clips, full-length feature films, news releases, and Voice of America broadcasts to explain the space program to the world. It arranges astronaut tours in conjunction with NASA and the State Department and works with NASA on the display of lunar samples. Its photographers and reporters are generally accredited and are treated as are all correspondents to NASA missions.

NASA and the Press

NASA's credibility has seldom been in question. Its handling of the story of the Apollo 204 fire raised a few eyebrows, but the much criticized delays in releasing the news were due largely to the necessity of first notifying the families of the astronauts. The fire had an effect on the working press that was not totally unexpected. For the first time the press became more critical and less willing to accept NASA information at face value. At the same time, NASA became more soul-searching. Today the press is recognized by NASA as not simply a necessary evil. Other agencies look at NASA's press relations with some envy, but few of them have NASA's glamour.

It has been the press that has made the greatest change in NASA information policy. In 1963, as Mercury ended, newsmen truly had to be satisfied with a few crumbs. The Mercury astronauts made no public appearances. Interviews were not possible after a postflight news conference. In 1971, the Apollo astronauts made 900 appearances, and each Apollo team devoted three interview days to the press. During Project Mercury all voice tapes from lift-off were on a delayed basis; on Apollo, radio and television were all in "real time" (as they occurred). In the Mercury orbital program no reporters were allowed in the Manned Spacecraft Center's Mission Control. With the advent of Gemini's two-man orbital flights in 1965, a pool of reporters (one reporter representing each medium) was allowed in the firing rooms at Cape Kennedy and in Mission Control. In the Mercury program, launch and control teams were not allowed to speak to the press, but briefings were held for the press at the change of each Gemini and Apollo shift. During Project Mercury, press kits were distributed shortly in advance of each mission, since timetables were kept secret thirty days prior to a launch. Now launch dates are announced several years in advance.

Prior to the excellent television coverage made possible by an improved color camera carried on the Lunar Rover during the July, 1971, Apollo 15 Mission, NASA and the public depended on the spectacular photographs taken by the astronauts themselves for a detailed look at what the flight crews saw during a mission. The NASA Audio-Visual Division has been responsible for releasing some of the most breathtaking pictures ever taken, ranging from the pictures of John Glenn taken by an automatic camera in his capsule to the amazing pictures of the "earthrise" taken by the crew of Apollo 8 as they orbited the moon.

In 1971 NASA released 3,167 black-and-white pictures and 3,912 color photographs. More than 500,000 copies of these photographs were distributed to the press. In the same year, some 11,000 copies of 251 film clips were distributed and about 176,000 copies of 718 audio tapes.

For a more personal examination of space flight and space flight facilities, the general public may visit the John F. Kennedy Space Center in Florida and the Manned Spacecraft Center in Houston, Texas. The center at Cape Kennedy is a huge, rambling display area with bus tours, numerous exhibits, and a shop where the visitor can purchase almost anything related to space. A motion picture theatre and lecture hall round out the facility. Present capacity of the visitor center at the Cape is 3,000 daily. Almost 2 million people have toured the facility already. NASA has asked Congress for funds to enlarge the visitor capacity to 20,000 daily, convinced that, while the facilities are overtaxed now, the situation will become more severe as increasing numbers of tourists flock to Disney World, only fifty miles to the west.

Almost a million people have gone through the ultra-contemporary Manned Spacecraft Center at Houston, which looks more like a college campus than a space command center.

COVERING A LAUNCH

The interest of the press in the space program never reached what could be called a low ebb. Some 200 professional and clerical employees constitute the Public Affairs Division of NASA. To date, 40,000 correspondents and photographers have been accredited to American space flights. Information people are brought from all sections of the country to "work" every launch event.

The process of accreditation begins about two months in advance. The correspondent hoping to cover an Apollo flight must first apply for his accreditation, make sure he can book a room near the Cape (often this is impossible), and prepare himself for a rather rigorous assignment. After registering at the news center, the reporter's first activity is to tour the Space Center and visit all of the major facilities. Having thus established a "feel" for the place, he is free to drive to the launch press site, where bleachers, television studios, a giant digital clock, and loud-speakers keep him informed about progress. Buses are available to serve all areas of the Space Center, from the news center to, on occasion, the VIP viewing area. Although the press must remain three and a half miles from the launch pad, the lift-off is clearly visible because of the huge size of the space vehicles. Shortly after lift-off, the press corps is flown to Mission Control in Houston.

Usually several hundred contractor public relations people man hotel suites and news center offices during a launch. Contractors such as North American (Apollo), Grumman (Lunar Module), and Boeing (Saturn V) provide coffee and air-conditioned offices for the working press. Frequently the most popular give-away with the press is not liquor but buttons and duplication mission patches. Covering a launch at the Cape, with its built-in drama and recreational benefits, is considered a top assignment by the working press.

PUBLIC RELATIONS

Recognizing the value of political power, NASA treats its detractors with as much respect as its supporters and, if possible, attempts to influence their decisions by trying to get them to witness as much of the program personally as possible. With the extensive cooperation of the military, NASA flies visiting VIP's to launches, treating them with tours, briefings, and other courtesies.

NASA's public relations program has touched most Americans. In 1971, 6,150,118 persons viewed NASA-produced films, not including those shown on television. In the same year, more than a million educational publications were distributed to young people throughout the world—719,639 in the U.S., 346,691 abroad. Spacemobile exhibits were viewed by almost 2 million children. The astronauts were seen by 771,297 people in 1971, and NASA speakers addressed an audience of 176,133. Inquiries totaled 223,864; 5,181 were not answered by NASA but referred to other agencies or to contractors, some of whom maintain public relations staffs in Washington for the purpose of selling the space program both to the working press and to Congress.

Despite these impressive statistics, which are second to those of no other agency, NASA has been charged with not selling the space program hard enough. In the early days, President Kennedy urged a more dramatic approach to manned flights, and the astronauts themselves took up their own cause. However, some congressmen and contractors have always believed that NASA cannot let the program be judged by public reaction alone.

As frustration over the Vietnam War increased and the NASA budget was slashed, polls demonstrated that the cutbacks were approved by the American people and, more alarming still, that fewer college students and young people supported a national program of space exploration. NASA's reaction to this was to send astronauts to universities for forums on space. Unfortunately, the astronauts looked terribly "establishment" to the young people and may have damaged the program even further.

What seems to disturb the NASA public information staff most is the overwhelming influence of the dozen or so television commentators who cover the space launches. The staff fears that a newsman's intonation or the expression on a TV reporter's face can irretrievably damage the coverage. Television reportage sometimes gives the wrong impression of a launch. In the Mercury program, the vehicles appeared as large as those that were used for the Apollo missions, which they were not. It is impossible to convey on a tiny screen what it actually "feels" like to see a towering launch vehicle lift off for the moon. These fears of the NASA staff could well be justified, but the networks argue that it is up to the American people to decide; if television is the medium they choose for news coverage of space exploration, then every effort must be made to provide diversity in the coverage.

Few problems have arisen with the press during launch events. It is usually during dull periods or between flights that an astronaut leaks a story, or a newsman discovers that an administrative change was caused due to a personality clash. Most government agencies will not even admit that such things happen, but on most occasions NASA not only admits such events but takes them in its stride.

In the early days the astronauts themselves were of primary public interest. With only seven astronauts, hero identification was easy for the public. The seven were admired by everyone from the President on down. The newer astronauts seem to the public and to the press to have less personality, simply because there are so many more of them. The two-man and three-man missions make it difficult for the public to keep track of the names. It did not help the situation when some astronauts left the program in anger. Gordon Cooper's farewell address indicted NASA for selecting Alan Shepard over him for a lunar flight. At the time, Cooper and Shepard were the only active astronauts from the original Mercury group. When some scientists and astronauts began to leave the program due to the lack of emphasis on scientific experiments in lunar missions, NASA protested meekly that "engineering flights" still merited highest priority.

Currently NASA is attempting to popularize the idea of a re-usable vehicle like the Space Shuttle and the fact that, with the advent of the Shuttle, space flight will become an everyday activity. A NASA spokesman recently objected to such public relations efforts in these words:

> Our job is to build the tools for space. We provide the transportation and the technology. We were never supposed to be responsible for the ultimate use of what we do. After we develop the Space Shuttle, perhaps we should go on to the next improvement, but the Shuttle will give the public a whole new image of the business, and the glamour by then will really have worn off and we will be down to the nuts and bolts of the reasons for having this program.

The Public Information Division is now shifting its efforts from promoting Apollo to selling the idea of the manned and unmanned earth resources programs. The difficulty of explaining to the public complicated scientific programs will manifest itself in this area more than in any other.

SCIENTIFIC AND TECHNICAL INFORMATION

The technical information people at NASA—whose duties should not be confused with those of the public information staff—look on their role as twofold: storage and dissemination of information of value to science and technology. The NASA Information Bank contains over half a million scientific and technical documents, journal articles, and reviews.

Thousands more are added each month. The material comes from grantholders, contractors, subcontractors, field centers, and the scientific press. Material exchanged with other countries is also stored in the Information Bank.

Merely recording this information is a major task in itself. The work is done at the NASA Scientific and Technical Information Facility at College Park, Maryland. Here documents are examined for relevance, checked to avoid duplication, and cataloged with a brief description. Each document is given an accession number, keyed to a bibliography in the NASA Information Bank computer so that each item can be located quickly.

Newly acquired documents are announced and summarized in two widely circulated semimonthly publications—*Scientific and Technical Aerospace Reports* (STAR) and *International Aerospace Abstracts* (IAA). STAR may be ordered through the Superintendent of Documents, U.S. Government Printing Office, Washington, D.C. 20402. IAA is available from the American Institute of Aeronautics and Astronautics, 750 Third Avenue, New York, New York 10017.

Specific queries originating outside the agency may be answered by computer searches through six regional dissemination centers operated for NASA by the University of Southern California, the University of New Mexico, Indiana University, the University of Pittsburgh, the University of Connecticut, and the North Carolina Science and Technology Research Center. "Interest profiles" are prepared for clients and used to select appropriate material as it becomes available.

THE PUBLICATION AND FILM PROGRAM

NASA's huge publication program ranges from a technical series to a series of picture reports featuring excellent color reproductions of NASA activities and missions. It includes technical reports that are relatively complete, technical reports more restricted in scope, translations of scientific and technical reports, reports on NASA-sponsored investigations, and "Special Publications." Special Publications designates illustrated reports and books of interest to the general public. Most of these are available from the Superintendent of Documents, U.S. Government Printing Office.

Another important series of publications originates in the Technology Utilization Division—the *Tech Briefs*. These are one- and two-page announcements of innovations, concepts, devices, and techniques. Many state a problem and its solution and list further information sources. Some are issued jointly by NASA and the Atomic Energy Commission. *Tech Briefs* are made available by the National Technical Information Service, Code 410.14, Springfield, Virginia 22151.

NASA maintains a long and very complete list of films about its activities that can be borrowed or purchased. The films are made available to television stations for unsponsored telecasts. Information about the films may be obtained by writing NASA, Film Library, National Audio Visual Center (GSA), Washington, D.C. 20409. Audio tapes are available from the same source.

In addition to the educational programs of the Public Information Division, discussed in Chapter III, NASA operates an extensive publications and film program aimed at the classroom. Such items as Apollo wall posters and picture sets are distributed to schools and private organizations. The *NASA Facts* series covers programs from Launch Vehicles to Food for Space Flight. NASA also publishes and makes available curriculum source materials and general educational materials with such titles as *Introducing Children to Space, Space Resources for Teachers—Chemistry, This Is NASA*, and *Log of Apollo 11*.

The problem of promoting NASA and its programs is becoming more difficult. Just how difficult is suggested by a former editor of *Life* magazine, whose present reaction to

NASA is: "I have seen too much of it, and frankly it bores me. It shouldn't, but it bores me." Part of the problem is that NASA has done such a good job in the past that space flight has become almost routine. NASA's honeymoon with the U.S. public is very much over. The 1960's were a very special time. Now all that is changed, and in the 1970's NASA's information personnel must show the American people—and Congress—why space should still be high on the list of national priorities. Just how good a job they do will be determined by the public and congressional support the NASA program receives in the years ahead.

XI

Controversies

Some critics of NASA say space exploration should be eliminated altogether. Others say that only manned exploration should be cut from the program. Because the political and scientific goal of landing a man on the moon and returning him to earth in the 1960's has already been met, a few critics ask: Why bother going on? Some critics contend that NASA's budget should be expended in areas of national social need, such as cancer research or population control.

THE GREAT DEBATE

The most repeated argument of the critics of NASA is: We have so many problems on earth, these should be solved before we explore space. This is the argument that disturbs NASA the most since it creates an unbridgeable gulf between the proponents and opponents of space exploration.

Members of the "reordering of priorities school" believe that technology has had its day. They reject the concept that a pluralistic society can meet its responsibility both to improve the social order and to expand human knowledge, and they insist that the problems of the cities, the problems of education, and other social problems are so severe that nothing but a total halt of aerospace work and a total redirection of national effort will meet society's need. When the benefits outlined in the following chapter are brought to their attention, they counter that such benefits are luxuries that our society can ill afford.

The words of a founder of the Soviet space program sum up the problem of priorities. Writing in the weekly *Novoye Vremya,* Leonid Sedov answered critics of the Soviet program—of whom there are many—by saying:

> One runs into the point of view that space research is a luxury and that heavy allocations spent on it should be supplied to the critical needs of earth—the fight against hunger and disease, the development of education, agriculture, and so forth. I cannot agree with that. . . . One must not forget that progress in fundamental science inevitably leads in many cases to a revolution in technology and the daily life of all people. A country which in our epoch ignores this truth dooms itself sooner or later to lagging behind in science and technology.

There is no question that if we are to survive we are going to have to manage our problems on earth in a much better way than we do now. Yet, it is fairly obvious to most politicians that if NASA were eliminated tomorrow its funds would not be redirected toward some more noble goal. Americans who are not willing to spend the money to explore space are no more likely to put this money into rebuilding capital or instituting a guaranteed annual income scheme. The public is tired of huge tax bills and small results. Their prejudice is not specifically against NASA but against federal government spending in general.

The question of national priorities is largely academic. It will only be solved by executive decision or democratic election. In the meantime, the critics of the space program and those who run it have much to learn from one another. The

178   NATIONAL AERONAUTICS AND SPACE ADMINISTRATION

critics of the program must face the fact that the very people
they rake over the coals are the men and women who have
the management ability to set a deadline and solve a problem.
This ability is what NASA is all about in terms of human
factors. NASA, for its part, must explain its position more
articulately. There is much wrong with the way NASA has
been answering its critics. For many years, NASA has attempted to justify space exploration by pointing to "spinoff,"
the technological by-products of its program that are applicable to other uses. This is a terribly serious error. NASA
should frankly justify its programs on the basis of their contributions to science and man's need to improve his lot by
doing something that he has never done before. NASA's supporters have not been honest, and it is this that critics should
take issue with.

It seems absurd that NASA has had to make so many
tough decisions before the eyes of the world and is so timid
about proclaiming the reason for its own existence. The one
argument that NASA has failed to use concerns the U.S.
investment in space. For $40 billion America has purchased
the ability to go into space, to make use of it, and to benefit
from it. Now, after this long period of investment, we are
almost ready to collect the payoff, but to do so we must
invest perhaps $8 billion more for a reusable space system.
Space is expensive only because we stand on the threshold,
not of a research and development program, but of an operational space effort in which we intend not simply to explore
but to exploit the new frontier. The question now becomes:
Shall we continue the program or abandon our investment?
It might be put even more succinctly: Can we afford not to
explore space? The debate about the usefulness of space exploration will no doubt continue, but there are a number of
lesser controversies concerning such aspects of NASA's long-
term programs as manned versus unmanned flight, the re-
usable Space Shuttle, military uses of space, and spending
levels.

MANNED VS. UNMANNED SPACE FLIGHT

The immortality of James Van Allen was assured in 1958 when experiments aboard the first American satellite, Explorer I, demonstrated that belts of intense radiation, named after Van Allen, surround the globe. Since that time Dr. Van Allen has spent the greater part of his public career promoting unmanned, or robot, space flight and calling for an end to the "expensive and dangerous proposition that a man must work in space."

Van Allen's premise is that space should be left to scientists, not to explorers and adventurers. It is an interesting argument, but many good arguments have been made both for unmanned and for manned exploration.

The proponents of unmanned space flight argue that it is less expensive, safer, and requires fewer national resources, less ground support, and smaller launch vehicles than does manned flight. Opponents contend that unmanned flight limits a mission's capabilities and is expensive compared to what the eventual cost of manned flight will be when backed up by the Space Shuttle. A single malfunction in unmanned flight can destroy an entire mission; electronic and optical observations are limited in scope; and space is looked upon as a medium for scientific discovery and experimentation rather than for human exploration and expansion. Manned flight, its supporters claim, results in many more scientific experiments per mission; man's versatility more than offsets the extensive safety and life-support features required, and his brain is the most versatile of all computers. Man can adjust and adapt, but a machine's adaptation is restricted to what man has previously programmed into it.

Space probes have given us incredible looks at Mars and Venus, but we still do not know what those planets are really like. The few grams of dust that the Soviet Luna returned from the moon do not compare to boulders collected by trained men. No machine can fix a stuck camera or replace a

broken valve. No robot can say what it is really like up there
on the moon in human terms.

In the Soviet Union the decision to continue with manned
space flight was based largely upon American successes. The
Luna automated probes of the moon were a remarkable accomplishment, but the Apollo 11 moon landing forced the
Soviets to attempt to excel in manned flight as well.

NASA's stand is that instrumented flight should be used
for routine or environmentally difficult jobs, and to assist
manned flight, as was done in the case of Ranger, Surveyor,
and the Lunar Orbiters, which supported Project Apollo. The
Office of Space Science is making every effort to compete
with the problem-ridden Office of Manned Space Flight. It is
this conflict that most concerns NASA. The Senate Space
Committee, deeply disturbed over this continuing difficulty,
is pressuring NASA into proposing further administrative
changes that would ease the competition.

The pleas from the Van Allen segment are for a more eco-
nomical program, and, unless the present trend changes, we
will wind up with an inexpensive instrumented space flight
program. Without manned space flight, space will become the
exclusive property of the controllers of robots and will cease
to encompass the promise of exploration that it holds out for
most of mankind.

THE SPACE SHUTTLE CONTROVERSY

The Space Shuttle is a reusable manned transportation
system that will replace the wide variety of boosters used in
manned and unmanned exploration today with a single vehicle. The Shuttle will have room aboard to carry passengers,
cargo, and spacecraft. It will have the ability to be launched
up to a hundred times with refurbishment similar to that a
jetliner undergoes between flights. The purpose of the Shuttle
is to reduce the enormous costs of launching objects into
space. It will be described in more detail in Chapter XIII.

The Shuttle, if funds for its development are forthcoming, will convert NASA's research and development launching program to an operational launching program. For the first time space costs will be reduced and the obsolescence problem of current hardware will be overcome. The present throwaway concept will be eliminated, and the initial $5.15 billion investment in the Shuttle will balance out in a short time depending upon how active the program is.

The Shuttle will allow a complete communications satellite system to be orbited not in eight or ten launches but in one launch. If a failure should occur in one satellite the Shuttle could retrieve it, and, if the problem is repairable aboard the orbiter element of the Shuttle, it can be put into operation again almost at once.

Those who argue in favor of the Shuttle claim that it is in effect the cheapest operational method for exploring space. Space would no longer be an experimental luxury. Even those calling for a total robot approach to space see value in the Shuttle because of its ability to orbit and retrieve robot spacecraft at a much lower cost than is presently possible.

Those opposed to the Shuttle compare it to the supersonic transport plane, claiming that it will give NASA a blank check for space exploration. Yet to completely develop the Shuttle will cost less than half of what was spent on the ill-fated supersonic transport. The Shuttle could be used for terrestrial flights as well. Passengers could be delivered any place on the planet within thirty minutes, and there would be little pollution because the vast majority of flights would be outside the atmosphere.

Military Implications of the Shuttle

While the Department of Defense has long been uninvolved with manned space flight, the Space Shuttle deeply interests the Pentagon. Two men in a militarily equipped space station could direct laser fire on communications, power, and defense facilities without warning. The Pentagon believes that an abandonment of the national space effort, led by the defeat of the Space Shuttle, could impair our ability to meet an aggressor's potential challenge.

NASA denies doing studies for the Department of Defense in military utilization of the Shuttle, but the fact remains that the Department and NASA have worked out a military version of the Shuttle for presentation to Congress. While this represents the worst possible use that could be made of the Space Shuttle, it does demonstrate the military versatility of a re-usable spacecraft.

How Much for Space?

No other federal agency has ever been required to conduct its operations in a fishbowl. The Department of Health, Education, and Welfare can bury its mistakes in a file, and the Defense Department can excuse a cost overrun equal to the entire NASA annual budget in the name of national security. Not NASA. NASA must prove itself before the eyes of the world with every mission. NASA was created in response to the cold war and then was given the most expensive peaceful venture of all times to carry out in a short period of time. Yet in little more than a decade NASA has put a man on the moon, has photographed the earth from space, and has established viable communications and weather satellite systems. For $40 billion we have gotten innumerable benefits and a feeling of national pride that Americans had thought they would never share again.

The most the United States has ever spent on space exploration in one year was $5.4 billion. That was in the mid-1960's at the height of the Gemini and Apollo programs. NASA estimates that several times that amount percolated through the national economy during that budget year in the form of wages, construction, and investments.

The current spending level of NASA is the least ever recommended by the President's Space Task Force. The budget squeeze, due primarily to the Vietnam War and the decrease in excitement over the space program, is likely to continue through the remainder of the 1970's. Perhaps the biggest loss due to the budget slashes is the Grand Tour flights that the Office of Space Science proposed for the late 1970's. This opportunity to visit the outer planets was very much a "once in a lifetime" opportunity.

Once the Space Shuttle is in operation (about 1980), manned flight will take on entirely new dimensions. It may be that NASA's efforts to demonstrate to the citizenry the benefits of space will by then have been so effective that criticizing space exploration will be like complaining about motherhood.

In the meantime, critics of NASA welcome the year-to-year battle for funds. NASA officials much prefer setting goals, getting funding for complete programs, and meeting deadlines. It is something they understand far better than the political ins and outs of annual budget fights. Until 1970 NASA had been tampered with from time to time but was, politically speaking, a virgin. Then President Nixon discovered that he could enhance his own prestige by appearing to actively support the program while at the same time cutting its budget. The President may well have permanently compromised NASA's political independence.

NASA's policy will change with the attitude of the man in the White House. Yet the capability of the agency has been established. Its staff is aware that it can do the big job on deadline, and it is this cockiness that serves as a vestige of hope for veterans of the agency. As Wernher von Braun puts it: "They will need us again."

XII

The Payoff

Space exploration is barely in its teens, yet in little more than a decade the United States has gone from orbiting a 30.8-pound satellite to sending 300,000-pound spaceships to the moon and back. The tremendous effort involved has had beneficial side effects—or, as some like to call them, spinoffs —that no one anticipated and that no one at first understood.

In the context of space, spinoff means that a technology developed for use in space is applicable to an almost totally unrelated field. (It has been NASA's misfortune to be remembered by most Americans as the developer of the material marketed as Corning Ware.) In the present decade, as NASA faces its most severe test to date, the first fruits of this technological harvest should be coming in. The impact of some of these benefits will be staggering. They may not only extend man's range but assure his survival. Others will be mere technological luxuries.

Wernher von Braun defined some of the benefits from the NASA programs before a Goddard Memorial Symposium in March, 1972: "I think it is extremely important that we Americans gain an understanding of how basic the development of high technology—especially high aerospace technology—is to our standard of living." He backed up his words by pointing to the favorable balance of trade in high-technology aerospace products as opposed to the unfavorable balance in low-technology products such as cars, textiles, and iron and steel. Annual U.S. exports over imports in aerospace products were then running at $3.6 billion, computers at $1.1 billion, and machinery at $1 billion. Motor vehicle imports over exports, however, were $3.3 billion, clothing and textiles $1.9 billion, and iron and steel also $1.9 billion. In these fields, von Braun pointed out, foreign imports are competing against labor costs—not high technology, in which this country excels.

NASA is not so foolish as to believe that none of the new technology would have happened had NASA not existed, but it is convinced that, without NASA, most of the new technology either would not have been developed or, if it had, that most of this knowledge would have moldered in scientists' notebooks and not been put to use. Space has stepped up the pace of world technology by years. It has advanced steadily and rapidly, and we have discovered things about our planet we preferred not to know, such as the really enormous problems created by the energy crisis.

President Lyndon Johnson once estimated that the United States will garner at least a 100 per cent return from its investment in space. Johnson was wise to point out, as NASA officials do, that the return will not be immediate. In fact, it may be so slow as not to be recognizable when it begins. However, the direct benefits that we enjoy today are obvious enough.

With massive opposition almost eliminating any chance of building the nuclear plants we will need for power sources by the century's end, NASA-sponsored research in spacecraft power sources is vital to all Americans. Pratt and Whitney, designer of the Apollo fuel cells, has contracted with twenty-eight gas utility companies for a fuel cell "black box" to provide power for the home. The black box could bring an end to the energy crisis and provide pollution-free power. An overload would not cause a massive power blackout—simply a temporary repair problem in one home, and utility rates could be adjusted on a more individual basis than at present.

With the Skylab space station ready for launching, the idea of manufacturing in a space environment no longer seems like fantasy. The manufacture of ball bearings in space is being studied closely by NASA, because only in space can a perfect sphere be manufactured. Attempts will also be made to manufacture and experiment with drugs and vaccines in an environment free of earthbound contamination. The manufacture of sophisticated medicines in space may provide an answer to manufacturing difficulties we have been unable to overcome on earth. Other highly critical manufacturing techniques will be studied in time.

In the area of research and development NASA has taken an old game and restructured it with new techniques and approaches. The time between research and application has been reduced by months and even years since NASA flew the first Mercury missions. A major spacecraft design change that required a year under Mercury technology could now be accomplished in weeks.

Space is a unique vantage point from which to observe or measure terrestrial phenomena. This is now done routinely by operational weather satellites, geodetic satellites, and earth resources survey satellites. Such space applications supplement existing technologies. For example, meteorological functions cannot be performed by satellites alone but they add important values to ground-based observations, and a communications satellite is of value only when supported by a dense communications network on the ground.

Despite the fact that America spends less than 1 per cent of the gross national product on space, the space program has given long-standing assistance to industry. Aerospace is our largest manufacturing area, employing more than 1.3 million Americans with a payroll of over $14 billion a year. Annually the aerospace industry does about $27 billion in business with a backlog in orders of some $25 billion.

Although the benefit to science itself from the space program is not considered great enough to justify the expense according to many critics, some of the results promise to be spectacular. Astronomical observations from the earth are becoming more difficult. The major telescopes are located near big cities. The glow of Los Angeles, for example, has strictly limited the value of Mount Wilson's 100-inch telescope. Space astronomy offers no such atmospheric obstacles, and both optical and electronic probing of the universe will teach us more about our own existence and our future. The Mariner probe forever erased romantic notions about the canals of Mars, and the moon has become a Rosetta stone with whose help we will someday be able to read the history of our own planet.

Space geodesy has led to some rather startling discoveries. It has confirmed that the earth wobbles on its axis and that we are living not on a globe but a pear! The earth has been mapped accurately, and we know where the atmosphere ends and the vacuum of space begins. The Van Allen radiation belt has changed our conceptions of space close to our planet, and the perspective of looking back at earth through a television camera has given us an idea of the vulnerability and insignificance of the "spaceship earth."

MEDICAL PROGRESS

In 1960 the area of medicine held the brightest promise of rapid progress, but it is here that the rate of return has been slowest. As we look back, we find only a few examples of the medical revolution that many reputable authorities predicted. Of late, new developments have appeared, some most encouraging. A NASA scientist, conducting basic research into the effects of ionizing space radiation on normal cell division, discovered intercellular linkages that may help to explain the behavior of certain types of cancer. A NASA–Stanford University team developed a computerized method of photographing a patient's diseased heart. The pictures can help the doctor identify dead tissue, scar tissue, and dysfunctions such as aneurysms. Stanford University and NASA have also developed a sonar method of monitoring a patient's heart rate and circulation. The sonar studies can be made by a technician in a matter of seconds.

A tiny analog computer developed by NASA's Lewis Research Center in Cleveland will assist doctors by continually monitoring changes in blood pressure and cardiac output. NASA has also developed a brain sensor in conjunction with test pilots that can assist in the diagnosis and treatment of schizophrenia. Using a radio transmitter, this tool can transmit the radical changes in brain pattern associated with schizophrenia. And a computer used to enhance details of photographs taken of other planets has been successfully used to analyze chromosomes in a human blood cell in three minutes, about one-tenth the time previously required.

Frequently hospital patients require the implantation of a breathing tube in the windpipe—a tracheotomy—and such patients must be monitored continuously by a nurse. Now a NASA-developed breathing sensor informs the intensive care unit of a blockage in time to save many patients from brain damage. The device, developed by Ames Research Center, notes differences in air temperature in the tube and turns on an audio and visual alarm within ten seconds of a change. The signal can be received either at a nurse's station or at an appropriate place in the patient's home.

A device called a transducer, about the size of a dime, was developed to measure landing impact speed when the Apollo spacecraft splashed down. This device, able to give both dynamic and static pressure readings, is now being used to assist in the precise measurement of pressure needed to fit artificial limbs.

Mylar, the material of which the 100-foot Echo I balloon was constructed, has been found to reflect 80 per cent of body heat. Mylar emergency rescue blankets are accordingly being widely manufactured.

The Ames Research Center developed a simple and accurate device that maps individual vision patterns. The device will prove to be a helpful diagnostic tool in assisting in the treatment of brain damage caused by tumors or other injuries, optic track degeneration, glaucoma and detached retina. This automated Visual Sensitivity Tester maps the location of the normal blind spot, whose characteristics reveal the condition of the patient's visual health.

At St. Luke's hospital in Denver, Colorado, the germ-control procedure used in purging spacecraft during production is now being used to lower risk of contamination in surgical procedures. The equipment includes helmets similar to those that astronauts wear and specially treated surgical clothing. The surgical clothing and helmet are connected to vacuum lines. An opening at the top of the helmet permits plenty of air to flow through to the nurses and the doctors, and headsets provide communication during surgical procedures. Surgeons are using this equipment in such major surgery as hip-joint replacements. It is of value in any surgical procedure where a large incision must be kept open for several hours.

NASA is currently developing a medical testing unit called the Integrated Medical and Behavioral Laboratory Measurement System. While the unit is designed for zero-gravity clinical support for an astronaut crew, earth applications are very much a part of its planning. Developed for long space missions, the unit will provide basic health services in the remoteness of outer space. A modified testing unit may have application in isolated and rural areas on earth where medical services are not currently available. The unit is designed to be run by a semiprofessional with help available for more complicated procedures by television and radio communication.

The hospital at the Huntsville, Alabama, field center will equip one of its rooms with a variety of NASA medical devices. When the room is completed, a totally immobile patient will be able to open and close doors and windows, operate a television set, control room climate, switch radio stations, use a dial telephone, adjust the position of the bed, signal a nurse, and even turn the pages of a book. A "sight switch," developed at the nearby George C. Marshall Center, plays a major role in operating the equipment. The patient can manipulate devices connected to this switch by merely looking into a sensor fitted to his eyeglasses. The foot-operated switch is so sensitive that a slight touch will trip it, and a breath switch can be operated by blowing against a tiny paddle. Total cost for this very advanced hospital room— $26,935.

BIOLOGY IN SPACE

Out of the Office of Space Science's biosatellite program has come a series of discoveries that may significantly add to the store of knowledge for use by medical researchers and in medical applications.

Biosatellite I, although successfully launched in 1966 with thirteen experiments, suffered a rocket failure after three days in operation, and recovery was impossible. Biosatellite II, launched in 1967, fared better, and its capsule was recovered after forty-five hours in orbit. Its principal finding was that weightlessness alters the orientation and normal functioning of plants. Damage to the hereditary material in the nucleus of plant cells was as much as two times greater when irradiation occurred in weightlessness. This raised an intriguing prospect that a better understanding of the mechanism of gravity in the internal affairs of cells may be used for practical purposes in enhancing radiation therapy for cancer.

Biosatellite III orbited a monkey from June 28 to July 7, 1969. A deterioration in the condition of the monkey necessitated recalling the capsule earlier than its planned thirty days' flight. Weightlessness had caused blood to pool in the central part of the monkey's body, and the monkey experienced a 20 per cent body weight loss, disruption of sleep patterns, disturbances of the eyes and the organs of balance, and a loss of skeletal calcium. Although the results could not be directly extrapolated to man, the changes tended to support some of the observations previously made in manned space flight.

Among the immediate benefits to the public at large from Biosatellite III were two technical advances. The first was a new kind of catheter with a minimal tendency to react chemically with and to irritate living tissue. The second was the surgical procedure developed for installing the catheters, which has since been used beneficially in human surgery. Still another result was the development of a synthetic liquid diet for laboratory specimens who fly in space capsules. This liquid required no digestion since it could be absorbed directly into the intestine. Adapted for human use, it has saved the lives of victims of acute gastro-intestinal failure, severe burns, and other injuries. All told, more than 150 developments with practical value in health care, food processing, and agriculture accrued from Biosatellite III.

Other programs of concern to bioscience are planetary quarantine, space health applications, gravitational biology, biological clocks and rhythms, orientation and navigation, and terrestrial ecology. Research has been pursued in such areas as increasing g-loading in centrifuges to limit the deposition of fat in the body, depressing body functions as protection against radiation, learning how the body uses protein

more effectively during certain hours, and designing procedures for the best use of the food that will have to be carried
aboard spacecraft for missions lasting several years. Such
findings may have immediate applicability by suggesting ways
of enhancing the efficiency of protein utilization on earth.
One surprising discovery has been that the brain's ability to
function well depends to a large extent on the kinds and
amount of protein consumed several hours earlier.

In the field of terrestrial ecology, bioscience research is
being directed toward understanding the processes whereby
various terrestrial flying and aquatic animals are able to filter
information, to identify, intercept, and avoid objects and
other animals, to discriminate faint signals, and to navigate
for long distances.

WEATHER SATELLITES

Accurate weather forecasting is worth money. In terms of
hard cash, it has been estimated that an accurate five-day
forecast saves between $2.5 and $5.5 billion a year in the
United States alone—and about $15 billion for the entire
world. Most of the savings are in agriculture, the construction industry, and flood control. Since the capital investment for a reliable global weather forecasting system is
priced at less than half a billion dollars, the payoff potential
is high.

Long before NASA, sounding rockets were furnishing data
on the upper atmosphere, but the earth satellite, by providing
layer viewing areas, has turned out to be a much more valuable meteorological tool. Like rockets and balloons, orbiting
satellites carrying instruments far above the layer of air that
hugs the ground afford an over-all view of the world's
weather.

The use of satellites to observe the earth's weather was
one of the first and best known earth-oriented applications of

space technology. The TIROS (Television and Infra-Red Observation Satellite) program developed the series of spacecraft used operationally by the National Oceanic and Atmospheric Administration, and NASA's Nimbus and Applications and Technology Satellites programs have prepared the way for the next generation of polar orbiting and geo-stationary meteorological satellites.

In pre-TIROS days, hurricanes used to sweep in from the unpatrolled areas of the oceans and slam into land areas with brief warnings. TIROS weather satellites have changed that situation by constantly monitoring cloud cover over desolate reaches of the ocean. Anyone who has watched TV news programs during the hurricane season has seen satellite pictures of these intense storms and has followed the progress of the storms as they struck land. Satellite pictures usually catch these storms in their formative stages, showing the prehurricane squall lines that ring a growing cloud nucleus.

Weather-watchers also benefit greatly from the automatic picture transmission cameras carried by U.S. weather satellites. These cameras take and immediately transmit pictures of the areas beneath the satellite to ground stations within a 2,000-mile range of the spacecraft. The pictures furnish local forecasters and ships at sea with an up-to-the-minute view of the cloud patterns over or adjacent to the local area. There are more than 500 ground station receivers located in over 50 countries around the world. The pictures received are used for local and area forecasts, route forecasts for aircraft flight, TV weather programs, newspaper weather reporting, and on occasions for routing supply ships through the Antarctic ice pack.

While the TIROS series of satellites were doing their operational chores, NASA was working on the Nimbus weather satellite, aimed at improving the instruments and spacecraft components used on the operational weather satellites. The Nimbus is a large, 1,400-pound automated spacecraft, four to five times the weight of the early TIROS. It has done pioneer work not only in cloud imaging but in measuring temperatures down to ground level.

Once NASA has developed weather and communications satellites, the responsibility for operations falls to other agencies of the government or to private industry. However, NASA still retains the task of finding ways and means to do that job better. This means testing improved instruments, improved means of keeping the station in orbit, and longer lifetimes for sensitive instrumentation and its supporting gear, such as tape recorders.

Often the only sure way to test a new camera or any other piece of space hardware is to put it on a satellite and try it out. For this reason, NASA has built a series of what are, in effect, multipurpose test beds—the Applications Technology Satellites (ATS).

ATS I, the first in the series launched December 6, 1966, was successfully placed into a synchronous equatorial (stationary) orbit over Christmas Island in the Pacific Ocean. Its most dramatic results were remarkably sharp pictures of the entire earth. From 22,300 miles up, its special cameras have taken thousands of pictures of circulation patterns in the atmosphere. Because it remains stationary over one area of the earth, it was able to provide long sequences of weather patterns in the development stages—such as typhoons, jet streams, and hurricane cells. In effect, ATS takes a movie of the weather over nearly 40 per cent of the earth, giving a perspective and timeliness that lower-orbiting weather satellites do not have.

Whether or not improved prediction techniques will lead to modification and eventual control of climatic changes is one of the key questions unanswered at this time. Needless to say, there are a host of problems attendant on such developments, with widespread international implications as well.

ATS II, launched April 5, 1967, failed to reach orbit, but

ATS III, launched November 5, 1967, was able to take full color pictures of the earth and to interrogate and to locate unmanned instrument platforms sending out oceanographic and weather data. Besides scrutinizing the earth below in visible light, satellites such as these can scan oceans and continents with infrared and microwave sensors. Since earth emissions of these signals depend upon surface temperatures and the composition of surface materials, the use of such sensors has interesting possibilities. These include agricultural census-taking and crop prediction. Different crops may be identified by their signals, as can their state of health and growth. This can lead to accurate forecasts of the world's food supplies, since diseases can be spotted early and countermeasures applied on the basis of satellite data. Forest fires can be spotted by temperature gradients even before smoke or flames erupt. Satellites can spot the upwelling of fresh water in coastal areas and can help in the planning of new dams for artificial waterways.

Satellites can quickly and cheaply survey huge areas of the world that have never been explored geologically and identify promising areas for mineral investigation that might have taken ground survey crews years to discover.

COMMUNICATIONS SATELLITES

The possibility for global communications via satellite was first described by the British writer Arthur C. Clarke in a 1945 article, "Extraterrestrial Relays," in *Wireless World*. Clarke pointed out that two small, artificial satellites in orbit high above the earth could relay messages between continents and greatly improve long-distance communication. Although he was known as a writer of science fiction, Clarke was ahead of his time by about fifteen years.

In its approach to space communications, NASA developed

three series of research and development satellites: Echo, Relay, and Syncom. The first was a balloon program, antedating NASA itself and originating in NACA's Langley Aeronautical Laboratory as an atmospheric research tool for the International Geophysical Year (1957–58). However, its potential as a passive radio reflector was quickly realized. Echo I was launched into a 1,052-mile space orbit on August 12, 1960. Echo II, 135 feet in diameter with an 816-mile orbit, was launched in 1964. By aiming transmitting and receiving antennas at the balloons, two-way voice and still-photo communications between the United States and Europe proved feasible. There was no limit to the number of users, and there were no parts to wear out, but the balloons did get wrinkled, and eventually they drifted down to earth in a fiery re-entry.

Despite their virtues, passive balloon satellites were passed up in favor of active repeaters. One reason for this, aside from the lack of control over users, was that a great many balloons—perhaps fifty in all—would have to be launched into low orbits to make communications on a global scale possible. The orbits had to be low, because signals reflected from high altitudes would be extremely weak. Balloon satellites do not amplify the signals, so ground stations must have large antennas and high-power transmitters.

To meet these problems, NASA developed Relay—a 4,600-mile, medium-altitude, active repeater communications system, and Syncom, which would hover in a 22,300-mile synchronous orbit above a fixed point on the earth. The American Telephone and Telegraph Company had an entry of its own design, Telstar, for which NASA supplied the launching services and ground-tracking facilities on a reimbursable basis.

To an engineer, the answer to the question of which kind of communications satellite system is best can be expressed only in terms of "trade-offs." He can put a satellite in higher orbit to gain wider coverage of the earth's surface, but he trades this for a loss in signal strength due to greater distance. Or he can add more power cells to the satellite at the expense of discarding one of the transmitters that increase the satellite's reliability.

Despite this dilemma, synchronous satellites emerged as the vehicles of choice, and NASA's Syncoms I, II, and III gave way to the Intelsat operational satellites of the Communications Satellite Corporation. Now that it is out of the operating field, NASA's communications role is that of providing research and development in antennas, multiple-access communications, and radio propagation.

An Applications Technology Satellite is being used by the Corporation for Public Broadcasting to allow a network linkup for educational stations across the nation at a fraction of microwave costs. The same ATS will be used for reliable ship-to-shore linkups on the high seas. ATS has also been tested for direct aircraft-to-satellite communication for transoceanic flights. Many communication experiments were conducted with the first ATS. It was used in a weather data relay experiment to disseminate data from a central facility to scattered weather stations via a synchronous satellite relay. It was used, too, for the first two-way, very high frequency communications between aircraft and the ground. This was important since it opened up possibilities for traffic control over the oceans and over sparsely populated land areas.

Communications satellites, such as Early Bird, which was launched many years ago, boosted the capacity of the trans-Atlantic phone system in its first three years of operation by 50 per cent. For the consumer this means that telephone service will drop in cost with every breakthrough. Each of the third series of Intelsat communications satellites carries 5,000 circuits yet costs only $9 million, including booster. An old-fashioned underwater cable system would cost $100 million and carry only 720 circuits.

AERONAUTICS

Not many years after the Wright brothers' first flight in 1903, America became complacent about the science of flight. When World War II began, we had no aircraft industry worth mentioning. After the war, the Soviets flew the first jet transport, not the Americans. NASA gave the United States a leadership position in air and space technology for the first time. All modern aircraft reflect a contribution from NASA, yet once we meet and surpass the challenge of another nation's technology we tend to fall back, waiting for the next assault on our national ego.

Aeronautics has found numerous benefits from the space program. NASA's work in conventional aircraft design is world renowned. New metals manufactured for the rigors of space flight have been used in stronger, lighter, and more functional aircraft. Without a space program, the huge 747 aircraft would not be in the air today.

NASA is currently involved in a joint effort with the Department of Transportation to reduce aircraft noise and airport area congestion. The goal of the project is to lower the noise level ten decibels each year until it is reduced to community background levels. NASA's major role in the program is to produce extremely quiet jet engines. NASA is also developing a system of computerized airline services for smaller cities and towns. The concept is called "dial-a-plane" and will work something like an air charter or air taxi service. The system will be based upon a computerized routing and passenger demand system.

To the aircraft industry, NASA's most important contribution is the development of the supercritical wing. This wing configuration will allow planes of the future to travel with less fuel, to carry much more weight, and to go much farther. Unlike conventional wings, the supercritical wing has an almost flat top and a curved bottom. This delays the rise in aerodynamic drag until the aircraft is flying at a higher rate of speed.

NASA will soon be flight-testing aircraft using the same command and control systems and the same instrumentation that guide Apollo to the moon and back. NASA's efforts will be felt by the private pilot also. General aviation lacks the facility for performing new research and adapting new technology. NASA, therefore, has contracted to have 10,000 documents of use to general aviation organized to facilitate the design of new light aircraft.

NASA is also busy developing quieter propulsion systems for STOL (Short Take-Off and Landing) aircraft. STOL aircraft may well be the quiet short-range transportation of the future. They must be pollution-free to meet NASA's goals (that includes noise pollution). A "clean" STOL engine is under development. NASA's Lewis Research Center in Cleveland is in charge of the continuing project.

A problem becoming more troublesome due to passenger freedom in the giant jumbo jets is clear air turbulence, which usually tosses an airplane around like a toy. While modern planes can withstand clear air turbulence, passengers cannot. NASA, working with the Department of Transportation, is using a B-57 aircraft at Edwards Air Force Base to search out and study such turbulence in the western part of the United States. Instruments on the aircraft can detect turbulence up to fifty miles ahead. At jet transport speeds, this early warning system would allow up to five minutes' warning time.

At Langley Research Center the first automatic helicopter landings are being conducted by NASA. The purpose is to give such aircraft the same safety margins that horizontal aircraft enjoy in poor visibility conditions.

A "pinger" has been developed to be deployed by a spacecraft automatically to make sea searches an easier task in case a vehicle lands off target. The Federal Aviation Administration is conducting research relevant to placing the automatic radio device in the flight log of all transoceanic aircraft. The pinger will continue to signal for five days and can be recovered from water as deep as 6,000 feet.

NASA's most impressive work in materials usage has been in safety areas. Bitter memories of the Apollo 204 fire remain, but no fire of that nature can happen again. NASA's work in fireproofing has changed the standards of the aerospace industry. Its family of fire-retardant materials includes paints, foam rubber, plastics, and cloth. Airlines are using these materials to make commercial flight safer.

OTHER APPLICATIONS

Spinoff depends on innovation. If a ceramic ablative can be used for a re-entry cone, why not for a kitchen pot? And so we have Corning Ware. From that earliest example of space technology transfer, we proceed to such items as the contour couch. If the contour couch makes it possible to subject an astronaut to 12 g's of pressure without injury, why not adapt the same system for use by a plane passenger whose spine might otherwise be shattered in the event of a plane crash?*

NASA and the Computer Industry

No other industry has grown quite like the computer industry, thanks to the requirements of space exploration. Without space exploration computers would still be an amusing novelty to most of us. Space, the most demanding of all appetites

---

* Another potential use for the astronauts' contour couch is in the area of automotive safety. A device based on the couch, now being tested by the Bureau of Public Roads, is both cheap and re-usable. It protects the rider from the effects of high-speed accidents. If the vehicle in which the passenger is riding is impacted at 60 miles an hour, the rider is subjected to the equivalent of a 5-mile-per-hour crash if he is tucked into the couch. The Ford Motor Company, among others, is incorporating this concept in test vehicles.

for fast and accurate information, forced the industry to generate smaller, faster, and more capable computers.

While rockets were still on the drawing boards, flight programs were being turned into computer "software." While arguments over valve construction of the Saturn were raging in Canoga Park and Huntsville, a program to check out launch pad operations by computer was being punched out. The software must come before the hardware, and without computers no moon rocket would leave the drafting table.

The techniques developed in fast data systems for the moon launch were sold to credit card companies and airlines for billing and reservation systems. The need for forced progress in the growth of the space program is obvious. In the Mercury program a man could be launched with a 40,000-word computer program. To launch an Apollo astronaut, a 1.5-million-word program was required.

The computer industry is now an $8-billion-a-year business and pays the highest average wage in American industry. In 1958, when NASA was born, the industry exported $48 million worth of computer hardware. Today we export more than a billion dollars' worth each year.

Earth Resources Technology

With much of the needed technology already in hand, NASA's first Earth Resources Technology Satellite was successfully launched in 1972, with a follow-up scheduled for 1973. Designed for polar orbit at an altitude of 575 miles, it is expected to conduct a variety of experiments in agriculture, oceanography, forestry, cartography, and other areas. It will be integrated with a ground data handling system to process the large volume of earth surface imagery produced. Plans are to operate the satellite over several seasons to verify its capability and to assess costs and results before proceeding with an operational system.

Earth Resources Technology Satellites make use of a relatively simple scientific fact: every object on earth, whether a mountain range, a road, or an agricultural crop, has a unique reflectivity. This reflectivity, as interpreted in photographs made from outer space, becomes a scientific tool with which to chart the object's future. NASA predicts a $4 billion a year saving on crop damage alone, based on information this program will provide. That figure already outstrips current space expenditures by almost a billion dollars.

Although there are more than 100 miles of space between an orbiting satellite and the sea, the satellite has turned out to be one of the most rewarding oceanographic tools yet devised. Cameras have monitored pollution patterns, beach erosion, river runoff, and sedimentation patterns. Temperature gradients in the sea have been determined and likely places for fish harvesting identified. Wave height, important for ship routing, can be measured over large ocean surfaces by sun glint from the sea surface.

The great corn blight of recent years has also concerned NASA. Working with the Department of Agriculture, a project was designed to have NASA monitor the developing stages of the blight and to study the possibilities of using remote sensing techniques to detect future outbreaks of the disease.

The government of Jamaica has asked NASA to assist in a survey of the country's resources. A specially instrumented aircraft has made flights over the island and its surrounding areas, and a formal report will give the Jamaican government an inventory of its natural resources so it can plot future growth.

In another international effort, Canada and the United States have agreed to use satellites jointly to survey each other's environment. Remote sensing devices will monitor air, water, land, forest, and crop conditions. The project will also map ice floes and ocean currents. Geologic, hydrologic, vegetation, and soil mapping studies will also be conducted.

A cooperative smog research program involving space scientists and California air pollution experts is under way, utilizing instruments and research techniques provided by the Ames Research Center in Mountainview, California. Flights of conventional aircraft will trace the photochemical production of pollutants and their dispersion in the atmosphere.

Pollution Research

While NASA awaited the launching of the Earth Resources Technology Satellite program, it conducted an airborne research program over four ecological test sites: one in Arizona, two in California, and one in the Chesapeake Bay area. The purpose of the program is to simulate as closely as possible the data output from satellites and provide scientists and equipment with a rehearsal of the Earth Resources Technology Satellite program. The spread of pollutants under various wind and terrain conditions can thus be studied with a view to better control.

The most welcome news to ecologists and those who are concerned about the decline of the planet is that NASA has developed a means of locating oil spills with airborne and spaceborne sensors. This means that in the future the earth resources project will be able to detect oil spills in the most remote places. With these detection skills available, those responsible for oil spills can be identified and punished under international agreement.

In the field of chemical pollution the chemicals that separate fuels in NASA boosters can now be used to separate oil from sea and fresh water. The same work in developing high-performance rocket nozzles can be applied to reducing industrial pollution.

The specific benefits of the above programs are too numerous to mention here. It is obvious that the by-products have been many and that NASA has made them very much available. NASA and Congress are not totally pleased with the aerospace industry's lack of initiative in selling many of these by-products to the country, but they are confident that the knowledge eventually will be used.

In 1970, a former NASA Administrator, Thomas Paine, told the Senate Committee on Aeronautical and Space Sciences:

> The best exhibits NASA could have here today, to convey to you in more dramatic terms the achievements and values produced in the last decade, would be Intelsat II communications satellite, a high-speed computer, a Saturn V rocket and Nimbus weather satellite, a Boeing 747, and a 210-foot tracking antenna. Perhaps the best exhibit of all would be to pile up $28 billion, representing the aerospace industry's order backlog, or assemble on the Capitol grounds the 50,000 Gulf Coast residents whose lives might have been lost to Camille without weather satellite detection and tracking. These are hard, tangible results from America's space program.

Technology Utilization

The most farsighted feature of the Space Act that created NASA was the generosity demonstrated by Congress in authorizing the agency to share its knowledge with the world. Administratively, the Office of Industry Affairs and Technology Utilization is responsible, along with the Public Information Division, for disseminating this knowledge on as wide a scale as possible.

The Office's Technology Utilization Division, with help from NASA's Inventions and Contributions Board, encourages the massive commercial use of new knowledge gained through space exploration. Technology application teams apply aerospace technology to problems in the public sector ranging from pollution to mine safety, from transportation to law enforcement. Biomedical applications teams have been set up at the Midwest Research Institute in Kansas City,

Missouri, and the Research Triangle Institute in San Antonio, Texas, to apply NASA data to medical and public health problems.

NASA makes its technology available to the public and to industry through six data dissemination service centers, located at the University of Southern California, the University of New Mexico, Indiana University, the University of Pittsburgh, and the University of Connecticut, and at the North Carolina Science and Technology Research Center. NASA's central computer can easily be tapped to supply information to any one of the six data dissemination centers. Each center employs a small staff and hires engineers on a part-time basis to assist with more specialized computer searches.

The space build-up has resulted in the establishment of no fewer than thirty-seven NASA-supported university research centers. NASA also runs COSMIC (Computer Software and Information Center) at the University of Georgia in Athens, Georgia, which makes computer programs available for reuse, thus saving the buyer about 90 per cent of the cost of a new program. To complement COSMIC, NASA and the European Space Research Organization have established a storage and retrieval data system, involving nearly 300 academic and governmental organizations.

Information on NASA or NASA-related patents can be obtained from the Patent Licensing Section of the Assistant General Counsel for Patent Matters at NASA Headquarters in Washington, D.C. For information about any other aspect of technological utilization, the Director of the Technical Utilization Division at NASA Headquarters should be contacted.

XIII

The Future of NASA

The great space drama of the 1960's is not apt to be repeated in the next decade. No President is issuing a call for Americans to visit a neighboring planet, and there is no ground-swell of national pride such as that which spurred us on to win the race to the moon in 1969. In that year a Space Task Force, chaired by Vice-President Spiro Agnew, made several recommendations regarding the future of NASA and offered President Richard Nixon three options.

Option A called for a massive $10-billion-a-year effort by 1975—a program that was summed up in one sentence: "The only limit to this is technology." Option C called for a $5.5 billion annual effort to take up where the Apollo program left off—at about half the cost of Option A but enough to build the Space Shuttle and provide groundwork for a manned Mars mission.

Richard Nixon selected neither of these. He chose Option B, the most modest effort, which requires an annual expenditure of $2.5 billion to $3 billion, calls for the end of all manned space flight by 1974, and severely restricts unmanned exploration of space. The President selected this option with the skill of a politician. NASA was no longer popular with

206

the public. Space was no longer so fascinating as it had been. Too little danger and too few failures had made technological miracles standard fare. The old popular political punch that had been NASA's chief congressional weapon was just not strong enough any more, and the President seized this opportunity to let the program wind down. Apollo 18 and 19, both highly scientific missions, were canceled. The Nixon administration claimed a saving of $200 million per flight, but it is difficult to understand the President's accounting methods. The ground support equipment and teams used for the moon missions will be broken up because of the cutbacks, yet these same teams will be needed when manned flight is resumed for the Space Shuttle. Unmanned flights also face serious cutbacks, and the proposals of the Office of Space Science for "grand tours" of the planets have been eliminated. If NASA gets the funding expected as of this writing, its future will be something like the following.

SKYLAB

For those who had followed NASA's programs through the years, 1972 was a year of nostalgia. Project Apollo—its commitment kept and its mandate gone—was relegated to history. The vast moonport facilities at launch complex 39 on Cape Kennedy were to be devoted to orbiting a 10,000-cubic-foot space station called Skylab aboard a two-stage Saturn V. That launch ends the career of the Saturn V.

The Saturn was scheduled to orbit the station without a crew in May, 1973. This project, born out of the labor of the 30,000 who have planned and built Skylab and its support facilities, has two main purposes: scientific investigations in earth orbit (solar astronomy, deep-space astronomy, space physics, biology) and economic and ecological applications (special photography, infrared imaging, and other techniques for gathering data on agriculture, oceanography, water management, forestry, geology, geography, air and water pollution, land use, and meteorology).

The Skylab space station consists of four major modules, all orbited at one time. The workshop module is the main unit and consists of crew quarters, galley, and storage and serves the many scientific needs of the mission. The airlock module makes it possible for the crew to egress from the workshop module and provides emergency docking facilities for rescue craft. It features a large working area and additional storage facilities. The telescope mount module is equipped with highly sophisticated telescopic instruments to study space free of earth's atmospheric shroud and light interference from urban centers. Its solar cells power other Skylab experiments as well as its own. It also carries computers and other equipment vital to the success of the mission. The fourth module, the multiple docking adapter, serves as the Skylab's "parking lot." Its compatible equipment will render it capable of accepting a Soviet spacecraft, since it is possible that a Soviet crew may visit the Skylab station during its lifetime.

The Skylab crew will be boosted into orbit by the smaller of the Saturn rocket series, which will lift off from the same facilities used by the large Saturn V. This is made possible by two giant "milkstools," which will give the 25-story booster a 120-foot lift on the two mobile launch pads, so it can utilize the same service tower as the Saturn V. Once launched, the crew will enjoy a roomier Apollo command module, since much equipment used in a moon launch will have been removed from the ship. By the time the crew ship approaches the Skylab station, it will have automatically deployed its foldable telescope mount. After twenty-eight days of working in space, the first crew will return to earth. The next mission will last the same length of time, and the third and final mission will last up to fifty-six days. The first flight will splash down in the Atlantic, and the last two will land in the Pacific.

A back-up Skylab and Saturn V booster will be available in the event of a launch abort. The second mobile launcher will carry a rescue rocket fitted with a special command module that features five crew spaces, two for the rescue team and three for the station crew. This all but eliminates the possibility of a stranded crew, like that portrayed in the technically excellent motion picture *Marooned*.

Skylab will for the first time team men with automatic spacecraft on more than an experimental scale. Working with the Earth Resources Technology Satellite program, Skylab will help to survey the earth. In conjunction with the Applications Technology Satellite program, the crews will conduct communication experiments and make observations that can be made in no other way.

Since a large inventory of Saturn launch vehicles will remain and since the Space Shuttle will not be tested before 1979, chances are excellent that the life of Skylab will be extended to ensure that astronaut and launch crew cohesion can be maintained until the Space Shuttle is ready.

THE SPACE SHUTTLE

The Space Shuttle, as an issue, has haunted the Nixon Administration. Sources close to the President report that the chief executive believed that aerospace workers who lost their jobs because of cuts in NASA's budget would find other jobs and the NASA program could slowly be phased down. As the unemployment problem continued during the President's first Administration, he made the political decision to give NASA the go-ahead on the Space Shuttle in the hope that his approval would strengthen his position for the 1972 Presidential election in California, a state hit hard by the NASA cutbacks of the early 1970's.

The White House urged NASA to locate both launch and recovery facilities for the Space Shuttle in California, but it now transpires that a polar orbit launch station will be set up by NASA at Vandenberg Air Force Base on the California coast, and the main launch facility for the Shuttle will be located at Cape Kennedy in Florida. Orbiter element landings will take place at first at such places as a new landing strip at Cape Kennedy and at Edwards Air Force Base in the Southern California desert. The vehicle assembly building and launch complex 39 at Cape Kennedy will be refurbished to service the Space Shuttle.

The President's go-ahead does not necessarily mean that the Space Shuttle will fly. The Shuttle faces a tough battle in Congress at every phase of development. NASA's original proposal for the Space Shuttle differed greatly from the limited vehicle that President Nixon has approved. Nevertheless, it is estimated that the Shuttle will generate some 50,000 jobs, although more may develop as the production program begins. The re-usable Shuttle vehicle may well become the workhorse of the national and international space programs and, in addition, may save the hundreds of millions of dollars that are being lost yearly through one-time use of boosters.

The Vehicle

The Shuttle was originally designed to be totally land recoverable. As NASA planned it, the Shuttle was to be made up of two stages, a booster element the size of a Boeing 747 airplane and an orbiter element the size of a Boeing 707. The elements would be launched vertically, and countdown and take-off would be automatic. A 65,000-pound payload would be carried in the large (15-by-60-foot) cargo bay of the orbiter element, rather than in the tip of the rocket. In its original design, the booster would lift the orbiter element to forty miles altitude, then separation would take place, and the booster element would switch to air-breathing engines and land at an airport. The orbiter would fire its rocket engines and go into low earth orbit and begin its work. The booster and orbiter would each have a two-man crew. After reaching orbit and performing its tasks (the orbiter element could change orbits at will) the orbiter would re-enter the earth's atmosphere and glide in for a landing on any long airport strip.

It is this sophisticated booster section of the Shuttle that NASA has been forced to cancel due to budget constraints.

The new booster element will be unmanned and about 175 feet long. It will feature two solid-fuel tanks 13 feet in diameter. Using a familiar NASA technique, the booster will drop off after it has finished its job and be parachuted to an ocean recovery by barge.

Few budget compromises have been made in the orbiter element. It will ride piggyback on the booster and will be roughly the size of a DC-9 aircraft (120 feet long with a wing span of 75 feet). The hatches will open very wide for large payloads. Since its cargo compartment will be pressurized the orbiter will be able to carry large amounts of cargo or people. It will feature engines of 550,000-pound thrust, as compared to the 1.5-million-pound thrust of the Saturn V engines. The Shuttle engines will be throttlable and will require very minor refurbishment following a mission.

The Manned Spacecraft Center in Houston will act as project manager for the Shuttle and is now completing final designs on the orbiter element. The Marshall Space Flight Center is developing the booster element, and the Kennedy Space Center will design and construct launch and recovery systems. The new vehicle will be able to fly up to a hundred missions and more with only limited refurbishment between flights. Fully fueled and ready for launch, the Shuttle will weigh almost 5 million pounds, about a million pounds less than the Saturn V/Apollo combination.

The government's investment in the Shuttle will result in huge savings. Each launch will cost about $10 million, much less than the cost of most of our instrument-carrying boosters.

This will reduce the cost of putting a payload in orbit from the present cost of $700 per pound to about $100.

But the Shuttle will do more than cut launch costs. Because spacecraft designers will not have to be so concerned with weight, new craft can be built with relatively inexpensive laboratory equipment instead of the very expensive miniaturized components presently in use. The Shuttle will make it possible for nonastronauts to fly into space, and the shirt-sleeve environment will allow passengers without rigorous astronaut training to fly. Above all, the Shuttle will make space operations routine.

To cut costs, NASA plans to make space available for commercial use of the vehicle. COMSAT, the Communications Satellite Corporation, will have its communications satellites launched and brought back for repair by the Shuttle. International uses of the Shuttle have already been discussed in Chapter IX.

NASA lists four main reasons for its decision to build the Space Shuttle: (1) the Shuttle is the only new meaningful manned program that can be accomplished on a modest budget; (2) the Shuttle will make space flight less complex and less costly; (3) the Shuttle is needed to do useful things; and (4) the Shuttle will encourage greater international participation in space flight.

In the spirit of the fourth reason, NASA has been in contact with various countries, including the Soviet Union, to see what chance there is of other countries contributing to the cost of constructing the Shuttle. It now looks as if European nations might contribute about 10 per cent of the total development cost. In return, NASA would orbit and service spacecraft of contributing nations.

The Space Shuttle is vital to the future of any NASA program. If a space station more sophisticated than Skylab is to be built, it must be put up in sections by the Shuttle. Further exploration of the moon and planets will depend upon the Shuttle. A mooncraft could be built in space and then launched into a lunar flight path from the orbit of the Shuttle. The possibilities are endless.

If the Shuttle proves itself, NASA is confident it can get funding for the more sophisticated booster element it originally planned to use.

The Space Tug and the Space Station

Following the development of the Shuttle, NASA plans to develop the Space Tug, a vehicle that would be even more useful than its earthbound, harbor-going counterpart. The tug would be carried into orbit aboard the Shuttle to supplement and extend the Shuttle's capabilities. It would be used to change spacecraft orbit, construct space stations, service spacecraft, and facilitate emergency repair work. NASA has reduced cost estimates of the Shuttle from $9 billion to $5.5 billion by cutting development and testing phases and by dropping the manned booster element and otherwise reducing the complexities of the vehicle. The space tug would cost an additional $600 million.

Beyond Skylab and the Space Shuttle is the modular Space Station.* The Space Station will have at least a ten-year life-span and will be constructed in modules, the first module being an independent station. The core module will weigh 100,000 pounds, contain five living and control decks, with two additional decks devoted to scientific experiments. The first module will accommodate twelve crew members. To keep crew morale high a great deal of care will be taken in selecting living facilities. Food served will be as near as possible to earth food. The station will have a complete galley and wardroom.

---

* While models of the station exist at NASA, anything beyond Skylab is conjecture at this point.

Once the station has proved itself, modules will be attached to form a large space base near earth. At first the base will accommodate fifty persons. This will be increased to a hundred. One version calls for artificial gravity in the station.

Originally the station was to be launched by a Saturn V in one flight. Now NASA plans to orbit the station in sections, using the Shuttle. Cost of the fully complemented Space Station will be about $7 billion. The earliest possible launch date will be 1980, unless the two remaining Saturn V vehicles are pressed into use for the project.

THE FUTURE OF SPACE SCIENCE

The Office of Space Science has some dramatic missions planned for the 1970's, beginning with its highly successful Mariner 9 project and its Orbiting Solar Observatory. It is now turning its attention to exploring the farthermost reaches of the solar system.

A 550-pound Pioneer F is on its way to explore the area beyond Mars, including the asteroid belt. During this trip, which will take two years and cover more than half a billion miles, the instruments will record the existence and density of helium, hydrogen atoms, electrons, hydrogen nuclei, and other elements necessary for life. Pioneer G will follow to Jupiter in late March, 1973.

To explore the area between Saturn and Pluto with one of our sophisticated vehicles would ordinarily take some thirty years. Late in the 1970's, however, the planets will align themselves in a unique way, and it will be possible for a spacecraft launched from earth to be bounced from the gravity field of one planet to another in the outer solar system in a fraction of the normal time. With just two flyby missions, all the outer planets could be reached. On the first flyby in 1976 and 1977, Jupiter, Saturn, and Pluto could be visited. On the second flyby in 1979, Jupiter, Uranus, and Neptune could be explored. To reach these planets will take much longer than other deep-space probes with which NASA has had experience. New spacecraft will be required for such extensive missions, already dubbed TOP (for Thermoelectric Outer Planets), captained by a STAR (Self Test and Repair) computer, a relative of the computer Hal in *2001, A Space Odyssey*. This 30-pound computer will be independent of earth command and will have a useful and operational life-span of at least ten years. The spacecraft, which can be used in orbital and flyby missions, will have a long-lasting atomic generator aboard designed by the Atomic Energy Commission. (TOP will be so far from the sun that solar power will not be feasible.)

The Office of Space Science is involved in some work closer to home. By the end of the 1970's, an air traffic control system will be orbited to make our airports safer. In coop-eration with the Federal Aviation Administration and the European Space Research Organization, the system is being planned to take some of the burden off air traffic controllers at major airports throughout the world. It will be invaluable for landing operations for the proposed Space Shuttle, which should be able to land at most large urban airports.

By the year 2000, demand for communications satellites will have eclipsed our current needs by 150 times, and the Applications Technology Satellites will make possible direct broadcasts from a satellite to the earth, no matter how remote the location. By then, an ATS should have been placed in stationary orbit over the Indian Ocean for India's exclusive use. NASA will have no control over what India programs on its satellite. Many educators believe that, because the techni-cal equipment needed for reception is so simple, the ATS could revolutionize education in the third world.

In the United States, the Applications Technology Satellites will serve remote towns and villages. No longer will rural schools be forced to play a second-rate role in education because of lack of money and facilities. An ATS will be used to launch the Biomedical Communications Network, linking health services across the United States, making it possible for a doctor to consult visually and orally with a distant hospital or colleagues at a moment's notice. Crime control will be improved by the transmission of statistics and fingerprints from one law enforcement agency to another in a matter of seconds.

Later in the present decade, ATS will launch huge 2,500-pound satellites to test new highly sophisticated communications techniques, using lasers. Geodetic and other science-oriented satellites will be launched as the decade progresses. As matters now stand, the Office of Space Science will prepare and launch the applications systems, and the Office of Applications will guide NASA in the use of these facilities.

A large High-Energy Astronomical Observatory (HEAO) will be orbited in the middle or late 1970's. The spacecraft will be 30 feet long and 9 feet in diameter and will weigh 10 tons. NASA expects the probe to reveal a great deal about energy in the universe. Weather satellites will reach new levels of sophistication in the 1970's. Better forecasts will be made possible by use of improved optics and instrumentation. If all goes well, the much delayed Viking program of the Office of Space Science will make a Mars landing in 1976 and send back pictures from the planet's surface via its orbiting transmitter.

All of the above programs, of course, depend upon the budget. If budget constraints are severe, Viking may be one of the first programs to be eliminated. It is possible that only the more practical satellites of the Office of Space Science will leave the earth. The more dramatic concepts may never leave the drawing board.

NASA AND THE SOVIETS

According to NASA, the Soviet Union spends twice what we do on space exploration and launches more than twice as many satellites and probes. Certainly the Soviets have demonstrated their prowess in automated and robot spacecraft. They have perfected automated soft landings on the lunar surface and on Mars and have impacted on Venus.

In the area of manned flight, the Soviet effort seems to have bogged down. Since the explosion of their 10-million-pound thrust booster on its launch pad, their manned flight program has not demonstrated much progress. The Soyuz spacecraft is crude by Apollo standards and apparently, after two major failures that have taken the lives of four cosmonauts, not particularly suited for near-earth missions.

The Soviets have orbited a small space station, about a fourth of the size of Skylab and far less sophisticated. The crew was killed after separation from the station, yet the Soviets continue to concentrate on manned flight by developing a space station.

In a way, the Soviet Union is responsible for creating NASA. It may well require a military turn in space to force action on the U.S. Congress for a full-speed-ahead program once again, but that is not likely as things stand. The Soviets will continue their work in testing communications satellites, launch planetary probes, and work toward an understanding with the United States and NASA. If NASA's plans for the Space Shuttle materialize, they may force the Soviets to ignore political differences and join the United States in the development of the Shuttle. Even the most ardent Marxist may have second thoughts about duplicating the work involved in this very expensive space transportation system.

So far, the most dramatic promise of space cooperation with the Soviet Union comes from the talks between NASA and Soviet space-program officials. NASA's goal, which was kept secret for the first few years of the meetings, is to fly a joint mission by 1975. Proponents of a joint program are under attack in both countries. Both groups face increasing pressure from the military but both desperately want to fly a practical earth-type mission together. As prospects look now, the 1975 deadline will be met. At meetings and working sessions in Houston and Moscow, agreements have been reached to standardize cabin atmosphere and docking equipment.

THE AVERAGE-MAN THEORY

When Alan Shepard flew his first Redstone/Mercury mission, we all wondered if we, the average people of this country, might some day climb aboard a spaceship and take off. It is clear that when the Space Shuttle does come along some of us nonastronauts will fly into space. Technicians will be needed, and the so-called average man will begin to play a part in a program thought up and fought for by men who were not average at all.

On the Shuttle, 3 g's (three times a person's earth weight) is the most a passenger will be subjected to, a force that most people can withstand. With life thus made "easier" in space and with average people going into orbit on a daily basis, the astronaut hero will be relegated to the pages of history. A few more may be used to colonize the planets, but chances are the planetary ships may simply be variations on the perfected Shuttle.

It is hard to imagine that a program that once involved 500,000 toilers—and now has only 150,000—will become the center of American attention again. Yet in 1958, when President Eisenhower purposely slowed and hindered the space program, few gave NASA much of a chance. To bet against this uniquely rugged agency would be foolish. If we as a people look outward again, it will be toward space. John Kennedy kept pounding home one theme that transcended politics and the cold war rhetoric in which he sometimes indulged, and that was the theme that space is the key to our future. Space may be the spirit that will move the coming generation to its full potential. If so, it will have found something besides war for which to work and plan.

It is easy to be critical of NASA. It incorporates elements of big business, power politics, and that *bête noire* of the environmentalists—modern technology. The critics of space are right when they say that we have high-priority items that need attention on earth. But it is the nature of human beings to want to do more than simply survive. That is why we went to the moon and why we want to go to the planets. NASA is like no other government agency. Other agencies take care of our practical needs; NASA does something about the human spirit too.

But the men of NASA are also practical. The get-tough policy the agency has decided to pursue in spite of its critics is reflected in these words by a deputy administrator: "People just don't understand how valuable space can be. We have to master it, now or later. If we do it now we can make life on earth a hell of a lot better for everyone. There are not many political loyalties in this agency, so if we fight, we will fight for the idea of space flight."

The creation of the Office of Space Applications is an indication that future programs of NASA will relate to the needs of the taxpayer as well as to science. Each element of society will benefit as the space harvest comes in. But the ultimate question is not one of value for money expended at all. One would be wise to ask where we would be if the Queen of Spain had said to Columbus, "No, the voyage is too expensive," or if the westbound settlers had been held back because too much remained to be done on the Eastern seaboard.

Our future in space faces the same sort of dilemma, but as long ago as 1963 the future was clearly perceived by one man, at least. On November 21, 1963, the next to the last day of his life, John Kennedy said in Texas:

A country as rich and powerful as this which bears so many burdens and responsibilities, which has so many opportunities, should be second to none.

There will be setbacks and frustrations and disappointments.

There will be, as there always are, pressures in this country to do less in this area as in so many others, and temptations to do something else that is perhaps easier. . . . This space effort must go on. The conquest of space must and will go ahead. That much we know. That much we can say with confidence and conviction.

Frank O'Conner, the Irish writer, tells in one of his books how, as a boy, he and his friends would make their way across the countryside, and when they came to an orchard wall that seemed too high and too doubtful to try and too difficult to permit their voyage to continue, they took off their hats and tossed them over the wall—and they had no choice but to follow them.

This nation has tossed its cap over the wall of space, and we have no choice but to follow it. Whatever the difficulties, they will be overcome. Whatever the hazards they must be guarded against. . . . With the help and support of all Americans, we will climb this wall with safety and speed—and we shall then explore the wonders on the other side.

Appendix A

A Career with NASA

More than any government agency, NASA offers diversity in job opportunities. Among the nearly 30,000 who work for the agency, one finds astronauts, secretaries, research scientists, technicians, historians, writers, experts in public relations and fire protection, photographers, and management people. The type of opportunity depends on the type of education. At NASA, a general educational background lends itself to management and related functions, and a scientific educational background leads to positions in the developmental aspects of the agency's programs.

AEROSPACE SCIENCE AND TECHNOLOGY

Positions in this category are concerned with the study and investigation of such specific subjects as aeronomy, the ionosphere, particle physics, meteors, the sun, moon, and planets, exobiology, instrumentation, materials and structures, fluid mechanics, data systems, life-support systems, and man-machine systems. Many such jobs are available only at the NASA facility or research center specializing in that discipline. The basic requirement for all technical and scientific positions is a bachelor's degree with a major in engineering, a physical science, a life science, or mathematics. A job applicant who did not complete a standard professional curriculum may nevertheless be eligible if he has obtained a graduate degree or has been accepted as a candidate for an advanced degree in a related field by an accredited institution. NASA's list of preferred college majors includes:

Architecture	Aeronautical Engineering
Astronautics	Ceramic Engineering
Astronomy	Chemical Engineering
Ceramics	Civil Engineering
Chemistry	Electrical Engineering
Electronics	Electronic Engineering
Geology	Engineering Mechanics
Geophysics	Engineering Physics
Mathematics	Industrial Engineering
Metallurgy	Mechanical Engineering
Meteorology	Metallurgical Engineering
Physics	Nuclear Engineering

Since requirements for NASA positions change from year to year, hard and fast rules about employment will not be included here. Those who graduated in the upper percentile of their class or distinguished themselves in some other way have a greater chance of being hired than those who did not.

ADMINISTRATION

Running NASA requires personnel with expertise in administrative operations, organization and management planning, project analysis and control, contract negotiation and administration, financial operations, personnel management, public information and news services, and technical publications. Administration is less rigid in educational requirements than the scientific disciplines. Here "experience counts a lot." While a college degree is desirable in administrative positions with NASA, the lack of a degree does not preclude an individual from rising among the administrative ranks to a top position. All applicants in this area, however, must meet one of three basic criteria: a bachelor's degree; the equivalent in experience; or graduate study of the type and level required for the applicant's speciality. For grade GS-13 and above, the applicant must have a clear understanding of research and development organization, structure, and problems.

STUDENTS

NASA will accept applications from students within nine months of meeting educational requirements for a NASA position. Students may receive and accept job offers prior to completion of academic requirements but may not begin work until requirements are completed. NASA will give credit for part-time or unpaid experience.

Basis of NASA Ratings

No written tests, save tests for a few accounting positions, are given at NASA. Qualifications are rated by NASA professionals serving as expert members of boards of U.S. Civil Service Examiners. Ratings are based on experience, education, and training as shown in the application for employment and on any additional information that the applicant is asked to provide. Lists of qualified candidates for positions are maintained but an application requires annual updating if the candidate is to remain on the list. NASA's employment practices are governed by the regulations of the Civil Service Commission.

How to Apply

College placement offices and the U.S. Civil Service Commission in the closest big city provide up-to-date information on how to apply for NASA positions. Each NASA research center has a board of examiners that selects the center's own employees according to Civil Service Commision guidelines. Would-be astronauts must submit a year-by-year tabulation of flight time and aircraft type. Further information may be obtained by writing the U.S. Civil Service Commission, Washington, D.C. 20415.

The Back Door

Working for NASA can lead to many rewarding and secure years with the agency, but students with appropriate qualifications should also consider employment with private corporations active in aerospace production. Frequently this kind of experience leads eventually to positions of major responsibilities within NASA. The reverse of course is true. Obviously if one were to spend several years with NASA, his chances of being hired by a private corporation involved in aerospace work would be greatly enhanced.

It would be wise for any applicant seeking employment with NASA to tour the facility at which he applies and to get to know its workings at firsthand if possible. The biggest complaint of NASA officials is: "Many applicants don't understand our goals or what NASA is. They would have a far better chance of being hired and doing a better job if they would take the time to get to know us first."

Appendix B

NASA International Activities– Summary

ANGOLA—meteorological satellites.

ANTIGUA—tracking and data acquisition stations.

ARGENTINA—sounding rockets, ionospheric satellites, weather satellites, meteorological satellites, communications satellites, earth renational fellowships, training at NASA centers, tracking and data acquisition stations.

ASCENSION ISLAND—tracking and data acquisition stations.

AUSTRALIA—sounding rockets, lunar sample analysis, ionospheric satellites, meteorological satellites, communications satellites, resident research associateships, training at centers, tracking and data acquisition stations.

AUSTRIA—ionospheric satellites, meteorological satellites, resident research associateships, international fellowships.

AZORES—meteorological satellites.

BAHREIN ISLANDS—meteorological satellites.

BELGIUM—lunar sample analysis, ionospheric satellites, meteorological satellites, resident research associateships, international fellowships.

BERMUDA—geodetic satellites, meteorological satellites.

BOLIVIA—ionospheric satellites.

BRAZIL—sounding rockets, lunar sample analysis, ionospheric satellites, meteorological satellites, communications satellites, earth resources programs, resident research associateships, international fellowships, training at centers, tracking and data acquisition stations.

BURMA—meteorological satellites.

CANADA—sounding rockets, lunar sample analysis, ionospheric satellites, geodetic satellites, meteorological satellites, communications satellites, earth resources programs, aeronautics, resident research associateships, training at centers, tracking and data acquisition stations.

CANTON ISLAND—tracking and data acquisition stations.

CEYLON—meteorological satellites, residential research associateships.

CHAD—meteorological satellites.

CHILE—ionospheric satellites, meteorological satellites, resident research associateships, training at centers, tracking and data acquisition stations.

CHINA, REPUBLIC OF—meteorological satellites, resident research associateships, tracking and data acquisition stations.

COLOMBIA—ionospheric satellites, meteorological satellites, resident research associateships.

COSTA RICA—meteorological satellites.

CYPRUS—meteorological satellites.

CZECHOSLOVAKIA—lunar sample analysis, geodetic satellites, meteorological satellites.

DENMARK—sounding rockets, ionospheric satellites, meteorological satellites, communications satellites, resident research associateships, international fellowships.

ECUADOR—training at centers, tracking and data acquisition stations.

EGYPT—meteorological satellites, resident research associateships.

EL SALVADOR—meteorological satellites.

ETHIOPIA—lunar sample analysis, meteorological satellites, training and data acquisition stations.

FIJI ISLANDS—meteorological satellites.

FINLAND—lunar sample analysis, ionospheric satellites, geodetic satellites, meteorological satellites, communications satellites.

FRANCE—experiments on NASA satellites, sounding rockets, lunar sample analysis, ionospheric satellites, geodetic satellites, meteorological satellites, aeronautics, resident research associateships, international fellowships, training at centers.

GERMANY, FEDERAL REPUBLIC OF—sounding rockets, lunar sample analysis, ionospheric satellites, geodetic satellites, meteorological satellites, communications satellites, earth resources programs, aeronautics, resident research associateships, international fellowships, training at centers, tracking and data acquisition stations.

GHANA—meteorological satellites.

GRAND BAHAMA—tracking and data acquisition stations.

GREECE—sounding rockets, ionospheric satellites, geodetic satellites, resident research associateships, tracking and data acquisition stations.

GREENLAND—ionospheric satellites, meteorological satellites.
GUADELOUPE—meteorological satellites.
HONG KONG—ionospheric satellites, meteorological satellites, resident research associateships.
HUNGARY—meteorological satellites.
ICELAND—meteorological satellites.
INDIA—sounding rockets, lunar sample analysis, ionospheric satellites, meteorological satellites, communications satellites, earth research programs, resident research associateships, international fellowships, training at centers, tracking and data acquisition stations.
INDONESIA—meteorological satellites.
IRAN—meteorological satellites, resident research associateships, tracking and data acquisition stations.
IRAQ—meteorological satellites.
IRELAND—meteorological satellites, resident research associateships.
ISRAEL—sounding rockets, ionospheric satellites, meteorological satellites, resident research associateships.
ITALY—experiments on NASA satellites, sounding rockets, lunar sample analysis, ionospheric satellites, meteorological satellites, resident research associateships, international fellowships, training at centers.
JAMAICA—ionospheric satellites, geodetic satellites, meteorological satellites.
JAPAN—sounding rockets, lunar sample analysis, ionospheric satellites, meteorological satellites, communications satellites, resident research associateships, international fellowships, training at centers, tracking and data acquisition stations.
KENYA—ionospheric satellites, meteorological satellites.
KOREA, SOUTH—lunar sample analysis, ionospheric satellites, meteorological satellites, resident research associateships.
MALAGASY—meteorological satellites, tracking and data acquisition stations.
MALAYSIA—ionospheric satellites, meteorological satellites.
MALDIVE ISLANDS—meteorological satellites.
MAURITIUS—meteorological satellites.
MEXICO—meteorological satellites, earth resources programs, resident research associateships, training at centers, international fellowships, tracking and data acquisition stations.
MOROCCO—meteorological satellites.
MOZAMBIQUE—meteorological satellites.
NETHERLANDS—experiments on NASA satellites, sounding rockets, ionospheric satellites, geodetic satellites, meteorological satellites, resident research associateships, international fellowships, training at centers, tracking and data acquisition stations.
NIGERIA—ionospheric satellites, tracking and data acquisition stations.

NORWAY—sounding rockets, lunar sample analysis, ionospheric satellites, geodetic satellites, meteorological satellites, communications satellites, resident research associateships, international fellowships, training at centers.

PAKISTAN—sounding rockets, ionospheric satellites, meteorological satellites, resident research associateships, international fellowships, training at centers.

PERU—ionospheric satellites, meteorological satellites, earth resources programs, international fellowships, training at centers, tracking and data acquisition stations.

PHILIPPINES—meteorological satellites, resident research associateships.

POLAND—meteorological satellites.

QATAR—meteorological satellites.

SENEGAL—meteorological satellites.

SINGAPORE—ionospheric satellites.

SOUTH AFRICA—lunar sample analysis, ionospheric satellites, meteorological satellites, resident research associateships, training at centers, tracking and data acquisition stations.

SOUTHERN RHODESIA—meteorological satellites.

SPAIN—sounding rockets, lunar sample analysis, ionospheric satellites, meteorological satellites, communications satellites, resident research associateships, international fellowships, training at centers, tracking and data acquisition stations.

SUDAN—ionospheric satellites, meteorological satellites.

SWEDEN—sounding rockets, ionospheric satellites, geodetic satellites, meteorological satellites, communications satellites, resident research associateships, international fellowships, training at centers.

SWITZERLAND—experiments on NASA satellites, lunar sample analysis, ionospheric satellites, geodetic satellites, meteorological satellites, resident research associateships, international fellowships.

TAHITI—meteorological satellites.

TANZANIA—ionospheric satellites, tracking and data acquisition satellites.

THAILAND—ionospheric satellites, meteorological satellites.

TURKEY—ionospheric satellites, meteorological satellites, resident research associateships.

UNION OF SOVIET SOCIALIST REPUBLICS—geodetic satellites, space rescue, joint manned flight, exchange lunar samples.

UNITED KINGDOM—experiments on NASA satellites, sounding rockets, lunar sample analysis, ionospheric satellites, geodetic satellites, meteorological satellites, communications satellites, aeronautics, resident research associateships, international fellowships, training at centers, tracking and data acquisition stations.

URUGUAY—resident research associateships.

VENEZUELA—resident research associateships.

VIETNAM, REPUBLIC OF—meteorological satellites.

YEMEN, SOUTHERN—meteorological satellites.

YUGOSLAVIA—meteorological satellites.

ZAMBIA—meteorological satellites.

Appendix C

U.S. and Soviet Manned Space Flights, 1961-71

The following data are from NASA's *Aeronautics and Space Report to the President: 1971 Activities*. Information on the Apollo 17 moon flight of December, 1972, is not included.

Spacecraft	Launch date	Crew	Flight time	Highlights
Vostok 1	Apr. 12, 1961	Yuri A. Gagarin	1 hr. 48 mins.	First manned flight.
Mercury-Redstone 3	May 5, 1961	Alan N. Shepard, Jr.	15 mins.	First U.S. flight; suborbital.
Mercury-Redstone 4	July 21, 1961	Virgil I. Grissom	16 mins.	Suborbital; capsule sank after landing.
Vostok 2	Aug. 6, 1961	Gherman S. Titov	25 hrs. 18 mins.	First flight exceeding 24 hrs.
Mercury-Atlas 6	Feb. 20, 1962	John H. Glenn, Jr.	4 hrs. 55 mins.	First American to orbit.
Mercury-Atlas 7	May 24, 1962	M. Scott Carpenter	4 hrs. 56 mins.	Landed 250 mi. from target.
Vostok 3	Aug. 11, 1962	Andrian G. Nikolayev	94 hrs. 22 mins.	First dual mission (with Vostok 4)
Vostok 4	Aug. 12, 1962	Pavel R. Popovich	70 hrs. 57 mins.	Came within 4 mi. of Vostok 3.
Mercury-Atlas 8	Oct. 3, 1962	Walter M. Schirra, Jr.	9 hrs. 13 mins.	Landed 5 mi. from target.
Mercury-Atlas 9	May 15, 1963	L. Gordon Cooper, Jr.	34 hrs. 20 mins.	First long U.S. flight.
Vostok 5	June 14, 1963	Valery F. Bykovsky	119 hrs. 6 mins.	Second dual mission (with Vostok 6).
Vostok 6	June 16, 1963	Valentina V. Tereshkova	70 hrs. 50 mins.	First woman in space; within 3 mi. of Vostok 5.
Voskhod 1	Oct. 12, 1964	Vladimir M. Komarov Konstantin P. Feoktistov Dr. Boris G. Yegorov	24 hrs. 17 mins.	First 3-man crew.

Voskhod 2	Mar. 18, 1965	Aleksei A. Leonov Pavel I. Belyayev	26 hrs. 2 mins.	First extravehicular activity (Leonov, 10 mins.).
Gemini 3	Mar. 23, 1965	Virgil I. Grissom John W. Young	4 hrs. 53 mins.	First U.S. 2-man flight; first manual maneuvers in orbit.
Gemini 4	June 3, 1965	James A. McDivitt Edward H. White, 2d	97 hrs. 56 mins.	21-minute extravehicular activity (White).
Gemini 5	Aug. 21, 1965	L. Gordon Cooper, Jr. Charles Conrad, Jr.	190 hrs. 55 mins.	Longest-duration manned flight to date.
Gemini 7	Dec. 4, 1965	Frank Borman James A. Lovell, Jr.	330 hrs. 35 mins.	Longest-duration manned flight.
Gemini 6-A	Dec. 15, 1965	Walter M. Schirra, Jr. Thomas P. Stafford	25 hrs. 51 mins.	Rendezvous within 1 foot of Gemini 7.
Gemini 8	Mar. 16, 1966	Neil A. Armstrong David R. Scott	10 hrs. 41 mins.	First docking of 2 orbiting space craft (Gemini 8 with Agena target rocket).
Gemini 9-A	June 3, 1966	Thomas P. Stafford Eugene A. Cernan	72 hrs. 21 mins.	Extravehicular activity; rendezvous.
Gemini 10	July 18, 1966	John W. Young Michael Collins	70 hrs. 47 mins.	First dual rendezvous (Gemini 10 with Agena 10, then Agena 8).
Gemini 11	Sept. 12, 1966	Charles Conrad, Jr. Richard F. Gordon, Jr.	71 hrs. 17 mins.	First initial-orbit rendezvous; first tethered flight; highest Earth-orbit altitude (853 miles).
Gemini 12	Nov. 11, 1966	James A. Lovell, Jr. Edwin E. Aldrin, Jr.	94 hrs. 35 mins.	Longest extravehicular activity (Aldrin, 5 hours 37 minutes).
Soyuz 1	Apr. 23, 1967	Vladimir M. Komarov	26 hrs. 37 mins.	Cosmonaut killed in reentry accident.
Apollo 7	Oct. 11, 1968	Walter M. Schirra, Jr. Donn F. Eisele R. Walter Cunningham	260 hrs. 9 mins.	First U.S. 3-man mission.
Soyuz 3	Oct. 26, 1968	Georgi Beregovoy	94 hrs. 51 mins.	Maneuvered near unmanned Soyuz 2.

Spacecraft	Launch date	Crew	Flight time	Highlights
Apollo 8	Dec. 21, 1968	Frank Borman James A. Lovell, Jr. William A. Anders	147 hrs. 1 min.	First manned orbit(s) of moon; first manned departure from earth's sphere of influence; highest speed ever attained in manned flight.
Soyuz 4 Soyuz 5	Jan. 14, 1969 Jan. 15, 1969	Vladimir Shatalov Boris Volynov Aleksey Yeliseyev Yevgeniv Khrunov	71 hrs, 23 mins. 72 hrs. 56 mins.	Soyuz 4 and 5 docked and transferred 2 Cosmonauts from Soyuz 5 to Soyuz 4.
Apollo 9	Mar. 3, 1969	James A. McDivitt David R. Scott Russell L. Schweickart	241 hrs. 1 min.	Successfully simulated in earth orbit operation of lunar module to landing and takeoff from lunar surface and rejoining with command module.
Apollo 10	May 18, 1969	Thomas P. Stafford John W. Young Eugene A. Cernan	192 hrs. 3 mins.	Successfully demonstrated complete system including lunar module descent to 47,000 ft. from the lunar surface.
Apollo 11	July 16, 1969	Neil A. Armstrong Michael Collins Edwin E. Aldrin, Jr.	195 hrs. 19 mins.	First manned landing on lunar surface and safe return to earth. First return of rock and soil samples to earth, and manned deployment of experiments on lunar surface.
Soyuz 6	Oct. 11, 1969	Georgiy Shonin Valeriy Kubasov	118 hrs. 42 mins.	Soyuz 6, 7 and 8 operated as a group flight without actually docking. Each conducted certain experiments, including welding and earth and celestial observations.
Soyuz 7	Oct. 12, 1969	Anatoliy Filipchencko Vladislav Volkov Viktor Gorbatko	118 hrs. 41 mins.	
Soyuz 8	Oct. 13, 1969	Vladimir Shatalov Aleksey Yeliseyev	118 hrs. 50 mins.	

Mission	Date	Crew	Duration	Description
Apollo 12	Nov. 14, 1969	Charles Conrad, Jr. Richard F. Gordon, Jr. Alan L. Bean	244 hrs. 36 mins.	Second manned lunar landing. Continued manned exploration and retrieved parts of Surveyor III spacecraft which landed in Ocean of Storms on Apr. 19, 1967.
Apollo 13	Apr. 11, 1970	James A. Lovell, Jr. Fred W. Haise, Jr. John L. Swigert, Jr.	142 hrs. 55 mins.	Mission aborted due to explosion in the service module. Ship circled moon, with crew using LEM as "lifeboat" until just prior to reentry.
Soyuz 9	June 1, 1970	Andrian G. Nikolayev Vitaliy I. Sevastianov	424 hrs. 59 mins.	Longest manned space flight lasting 17 days 16 hrs. 59 mins.
Apollo 14	Jan. 31, 1971	Alan B. Shepard Stuart A. Roosa Edgar D. Mitchell	216 hrs. 42 mins.	Third manned lunar landing. Mission demonstrated pin-point landing capability and continued manned exploration.
Soyuz 10	Apr. 22, 1971	Vladimir Shatalov Aleksey Yeliseyev Nikolai Rukavishnikov	47 hrs. 46 mins.	Docked with Salyut 1, but crew did not board space station launched April 19. Crew recovered Apr. 24, 1971.
Soyuz 11	June 6, 1971	Georgiy Timofeyevich Dobrovolskiy Vladislav Nikolayevich Volkov Viktor Ivanovich Patsayev	570 hrs. 22 mins.	Docked with Salyut 1 and Soyuz 11 crew occupied space station for 22 days. Crew perished during final phase of Soyuz 11 capsule recovery on June 30, 1971.
Apollo 15	July 26, 1971	David R. Scott Alfred M. Worden James Bensen Irwin	295 hrs. 11 mins. 53 secs.	Fourth manned lunar landing and first Apollo "J" series mission which carry the Lunar Roving Vehicle. Worden's in-flight EVA of 38 min. 12 secs. was performed during return trip.

233

Bibliography

BOOKS

BLOOMFIELD, LINCOLN P.; ed. *Outer Space: Prospects for Man and Society*. New York: Praeger, 1968.

KENNEDY, JOHN F.; edited by ALLAN NEVINS. *The Burden and the Glory*. New York: Harper and Row, 1964.

LAY, BERNIE, JR. *Earthbound Astronauts*. Englewood Cliffs, N.J.: Prentice-Hall, 1971.

MAILER, NORMAN. *Of a Fire on the Moon*. Boston: Little, Brown, 1970.

SCHLESINGER, ARTHUR, JR. *A Thousand Days*. Boston: Houghton Mifflin, 1965.

GOVERNMENT PUBLICATIONS

Published by the U.S. Government Printing
Office unless otherwise noted

CORLISS, WILLIAM R. *Nuclear Propulsion for Space*. Atomic Energy Commission, 1969.

KENNEDY, JOHN F. *The Public Papers of the President, 1961. 1962. 1963*. 3 vols., 1962–64.

U.S. HOUSE OF REPRESENTATIVES. COMMITTEE ON SCIENCE AND ASTRONAUTICS. *NASA Authorization Hearings*. Annual. 1959–73.

U.S. SENATE. COMMITTEE ON AERONAUTICAL AND SPACE SCIENCES. *NASA Authorization Hearings*. Annual. 1959–73.

————. ————. *Space Program Benefits: Hearings*. 1970.

————. ————. *Tenth Anniversary Report . . . 1958–68*. 1968.

THE WHITE HOUSE. *Aeronautics and Space Report of the President.* Annual. 1961–71.

NASA Publications

For the Benefit of All Mankind. 1972. Booklet.
International Programs of NASA. 1971.
NASA—America's Next Decade in Space: A Report for the Space Task Group. 1969.
NASA Annual Procurement Reports. 1959–71.
NASA Film List. 1971. Brochure.
NASA Scientific and Technical Information System. 1970. Booklet.
NASA 20th Century Explorer. 1966. Booklet.
ROSHOLT, ROBERT. *An Administrative History of NASA.* 1966.
A Study of NASA University Programs. 1970.
SWENSON, LLOYD S., JR., JAMES M. GRIMWOOD, and CHARLES C. ALEXANDER. *This New Ocean: A History of Project Mercury.* 1966.
This Is NASA. 1971. Booklet.

MISCELLANEOUS

Applications of Aerospace Technology in Industry. A series prepared by the Industrial Economics Division of the Denver Research Institute. University of Denver, 1971.
BUTZ, J. S., JR. "The Coming Age of Economy Flight in Space." *Air Force-Space Digest,* December, 1969.
HAGGERTY, JAMES J. "The Giant Harvest from Space—Today and Tomorrow." *Air Force-Space Digest,* February, 1970.
The Jet Propulsion Laboratory. Pasadena, Calif.: Jet Propulsion Laboratory, 1969.
LEAVITT, WILLIAM. "Ten Tumultuous Years—NASA's First Decade." *Air Force-Space Digest,* October, 1968.
"Legal Principles Governing the Activities of States in the Exploration and Use of Outer Space." New York: United Nations, December 24, 1963. Press release.
WICKER, TOM. "In the Nation: Reflections on Apollo." *New York Times,* March 18, 1969.
WILFORD, JOHN N. "Men Walk on Moon." *New York Times,* July 21, 1969.

Index